Still Going Strong

Still Going Strong

Richard Ingrams & John Wells

Illustrated by Brian Bagnall

PRIVATE EYE/ANDRE DEUTSCH

Published in Great Britain by Private Eye Productions Ltd,
6 Carlisle Street, London W1

In association with André Deutsch Ltd,
105–106 Great Russell Street, London WC1

© 1988 Pressdram Ltd
Illustrations by Brian Bagnall © 1988

ISBN 233 98336 8

Typeset by JH Graphics Ltd, Reading, Berks.

Printed by The Bath Press, Bath, Avon

Dear Bill,

Only a few hours before the nation goes to the urns for its tryst with Destiny. I must say I'm absolutely knackered. In the old days when we were allowed to mingle freely with the hoi polloi without fear of the assassin's bazooka there was always an egg or two flying through the air, some loony screaming in one's face or pouring treacle down the back of one's neck to jolly things along. However since the Big Security Clampdown it's worse than being in *The Mousetrap*. Only the Party Faithful are allowed within mortar range of the Boss, and as no one's supposed to know the venue in advance some of the poor buggers have been sitting about for days on end waiting for the fun to start.

I don't know if you've seen any of our Nuremberg Numbers on the TV, but what they show is only the half of it. A while back, Tebbit ran into some cove in a Happy Eater called Barlowe who used to organise evangelical rallies for that American skypilot friend of Hoppo's Billy Graham. (Do you remember the time Maurice tooled along to Wembley after a disastrous afternoon at cards? As I recall, he got very tearful during the hymn-singing, and when they asked for converts to leave their seats and make their witness he tottered forward, only to collapse insensate at the feet of the Evangelist. Maurice said he woke up in a ghastly little semi-detached in Willesden with some awful woman with a moustache leaning over him and pressing a lot of pamphlets into his hand advocating a Cleaner Life. Fat lot of good that did.)

Anyway this Barlow bird shot Tebbit a pretty good line, promising to do for the Boss what he'd done for Rev. Graham and before we knew it he was on the strength. The poor old Tory stalwarts didn't know what had hit them. Instead of having a few jars in the pub and then bindling down to the Village Hall for the Big Speech, they were all forced to parade stone cold sober three hours before Curtain Up in the nearest Conference Centre. Barlowe then came on the stage with his gag book and made them shake hands with each other, stand up, sit down, cheer, practise laughing and clapping and generally worked them up into a frenzy. Zero Hour Minus One they were subjected to strobe lighting, disorientation processes, and deafening music played through giant loudspeakers specially composed by that hairy chimpanzee who made all the money out of *Cats*. Meanwhile pictures of the Boss mingling with the Mighty were subliminally flashed at them and by the time the Royal Party reached the platform they were frothing at the mouth, waving their flags, wetting themselves and with no idea at all where they were.

Just as well, as it turned out, as the Boss's jokes, courtesy Sir Custardface, were even more abysmal than usual. Like all of us, I think he's beginning to feel the strain third time round and there was one joke about Roses I didn't understand at all. The audience, however, being in the state they were, broke furniture laughing, and when the Boss began to wave her big blue flag they went positively apeshit and Barlowe had to turn the sprinklers on. I was quite grateful for the SAS, or we might have been stripped to the buff.

All this Showbiz Razamataz was started by the other side, who brought in a lot of Wardour Street spivs from the film business to try and build up poor little Kinnock into some sort of balding Rambo of the Valleys with a heart of gold and a twinkle in his eye. Mr Sillybilly and Co. were told to bugger off and leave the stage to Superginge, who in the company of his lovely wife and various carefully chosen middle-class relatives, would soar above the sordid details of Life with Labour on wings of Welsh song.

Pillock himself was then put on the spot by that ghastly Frost man, married to the daughter of some Duke or other, who got him in a Chinese Knot on the CND issue, forcing Comrade Neil to outline his scenario for fighting off the Russian Bear with pick handles and non-cooperation.

Meanwhile Munster has been getting his arse chewed for continuing to promote the Corsican Twins, whose TV ads for our side have been utterly pathetic. In the one I saw Luigi was dressed up as a conjuror doing something disgusting with a pantomime horse, then more film of M. shaking hands with Hoppo, several wogs, and then Hoppo again. The fact that she is the only British politician the World's Oldest Gunslinger can recognise is the Saatchis' trump card, hence the last-minute dash to be snapped in a gondola with the old boy in that Eyetie sewage farm. Watch this space for news of the Corsicans' repatriation.

'. . . in a gondola with the old boy in that Eyetie
sewage farm . . .'

Poor old Batman and Robin seem to have vanished up that orifice into which the Woozlum Bird was last seen disappearing. Boris's poll of a thousand expatriate Russians revealed that they didn't like the idea of two people in charge, as sooner or later they would fall out, and that anyway, now all the Labour Party had taken to wearing suits, they couldn't tell the difference. I'm told that after a decent interval the Doctor will sign on with our lot and that Steel will retire to the Borders to form a closer relationship with the sheep. Shades of the Falklands, what?

Smarmy Cecil has been in casing the joint and I must say I

slightly blew my top. 'If that man moves in here,' I allowed myself to observe as he made his fond farewells last night, 'I am moving out. To Dulwich.' The Boss, who was putting her blue pencil through Sir Custardface's final list of gems, became, to my surprise, almost human for a moment. 'Oh Denis,' she soothed in the voice she normally reserves for that piss-artist with the bow-tie on the TV, 'don't think I haven't considered your feelings. Of course you must go. Another ten years in office and you'll be eighty-two. I cannot expect you to stay at my side until the bitter end. Of course you must enjoy the golden eventide with your friends, away from all the wear and tear of Downing Street. No, let me finish. Don't think I can't appreciate how nobly you have borne the unnatural life as my Duke of Edinburgh.'

Quite honestly, Bill, I was a bit put out. Can you imagine what she's up to?

Yours in the booth voting Labour,

DENIS

 10 Downing Street
Whitehall
26 JUNE 1987

Dear Bill,
As you may have gathered from the media, all my worst fears have been realised. Boss slavering to go on and on and on, Smarmy Cecil back in the saddle, and no earthly chance of putting the feet up in Dulwich. All I have before me now is a life sentence at Number Ten, rather like that poor old Johnny in Berlin.

Talking of the elderly, they finally managed to dump Pegleg Hailsham. They'd been putting it off, hoping the water torture would persuade Mogadon Man to mount the Woolsack, but the little bugger dug his heels in and they had to appoint that no-hoper Havers. It means he'll have to give up the afternoon drinking clubs and fritter away his dotage in the House of Lords, but I doubt if he'll notice the difference and he gets a very decent screw considering all he has to do is stay awake.

Poor Munster has been eased out, rather like Prosser-Cluff after the 'exposure' episode on the Chairman's lawn, and I couldn't help feeling sorry for him. He's been very loyal biting all those people in the leg for the Boss over the years. The final straw came on the famous Wobbly Thursday when it looked for one glorious moment as if Superginge was about to open my prison house door and sweep the Boss into oblivion. The old girl got very jittery and started to take it out on the wretched Corsicans who were accused of making her wear the wrong shoulder-pads and speak in a soft unnatural voice. Munster made the mistake of standing up for them and took great exception when they were forced to produce some ghastly little coke-sniffer in red-framed spectacles to take charge of the Final Push.

To cap it all, Smarmy C. began to shimmer about whispering in the Boss's ear like some ghastly floor-walker from Moss Bros. Result, voices raised in Corridors of Power, Munster queuing at Labour Exchange the following morning. By the way, Boris made quite a good joke about Cecil coming in as Minister of Energy, saying the only sort of energy he'd ever given evidence of was hammering the bedsprings. Not bad for a Russky.

Matters chez Batman and Robin have gone from bad to worse. They took a frightful drubbing at the polls; that fat old wine-bibber with the funny voice got the bum's rush along with the woman with messy hair and the dogfood man, the upshot being that the entire Alliance can now easily meet in one cubicle in the Gents without the need for extra chairs to be brought in. Robin is all for a merger, but Batman is dead set against it on the grounds that he would be obliged to hand over the black cape and mask to his little friend, a prospect which for obvious reasons does not appeal.

Meanwhile the Smellysocks are mysteriously triumphant, having gone round well under par and then skied their balls into the water at the eighteenth. Superginge is full of the joys and telling all his new troops, including various Moscow-trained coons and the Gay-boys' Friend from the GLC, that they've pulled off a big victory and must all stick together till '91 when they will reap their just rewards. What he doesn't seem able to haul in, being of limited intellect like a lot of Welsh ex-students, is that the aforementioned Newt-lover and the Broadwater Farm Brigade are even now grinding their axes

'. . . like some ghastly floor-walker from Moss Bros.'

in a shower of sparks preparing to sink them in his perfectly polished dome.

Have you seen your broker lately? Furniss's man panicked on June 10, switched all my funds to Bermuda on his magic box and is now having the devil's own job finding them again. Meanwhile the reptiles are trying to drag Charlie Whackett's name through the mire suggesting I am the Godfather of SW1. Ever since that big German who owns the *Observer* wasn't allowed to buy Harrods, he's been trying to smear me and Mark as some kind of twopenny ha'penny shysters mixed up with Mafia-type riff-raff and shady wogs of every hue. If it continues I shall have to give that libel lawyer of Munster's a bell. Shorter-Screw? Cutter-Fark? I've got it written down somewhere.

I'm sorry about the Wimbledon tickets, but apparently our normal source was rumbled by the Old Bill, so I am having to advertise in the *Telegraph*. See you at Worplesdon. Don't forget to bring your pills this time.

Yours in Spandau,

DENIS

 10 Downing Street
Whitehall

10 JULY 1987

Dear Bill,

I'm glad you both enjoyed our day at Wimbledon. I'm afraid I bumped into some Yankee friends of the Major's in the bar and got rather tied up, but I always find the picture on the TV gives one a much better idea of the game and one avoids getting either drenched or sunstroke. I thought the lesboes were hammering them down pretty well – though not as fast as yours truly. But it's all pretty tame since Superbrat hung up his clogs. Rather like coffee mornings at Downing Street without Heseltine.

Talking of whom, as you may have seen, our lot have run

into trouble over their plans to do away with the Rates. I started the ball rolling some time ago when we got our first quarterly instalment from Dulwich UDC for £3,500. Where does it all go, you may ask? The lion's share obviously on Trot schools giving the toddlers crash courses in Gay Studies – while the ordinary citizen like you or me derives sod all from it except inadequate street lighting and the privilege of pushing one's wheelie all the way to the bottom of the drive every Tuesday should the dustmen deign to stop by. Even then I had to have a stand-up altercation with some cockney lout who made insolent remarks about five binliners full of empty bottles. 'We been knocking it back again then? Celebrating Her Ladyship's victory or drowning our sorrows?' I told him not to be insolent but he only waved his finger and said, 'Now now, Den, mind the blood pressure.'

'. . . Now, now, Den . . .'

The point being, as I explained to that prat Ridley, that the whole burden of rates is borne by hard-working householders like yours truly with grown up children who have worked hard to get a decent-sized roof over their heads and a bit of room to spare, while scrimshankers just down the road in council houses, all earning, as we know, well in excess of a hundred thou. a year, and many of them drawing supplementary benefit and sleeping five to a room, pay sod all. I think little Ridley took it all on board, and after stabbing at his pocket calculator for a bit he came up with something called a Poll Tax, forcing the proles to pay their whack. Not surprisingly it hasn't gone down well with the Wets. The blue-rinsed Sailor Ted, who seems to have thrown in the perfumed sponge and retired to live in the Cathedral Close at Salisbury cheek by jowl with a lot of vicars and assorted trouser-pilots, re-emerged to berate the Boss for winning the election. Sour grapes weren't in it, Bill. Everything the old girl had ever turned her hand to was rubbish, why should kiddies pay for violin lessons, last time we had a Poll Tax in 1387 the Peasants Revolted and King John had to throw his undies in the Wash. All the Smellysocks stood up and cheered, Boss ignored him altogether and he had to shake hands with Heseltine in the tea-bar. Poor old bugger, though I can't say I feel sorry for him.

The Smellysocks also got very steamed up about that rat-faced Ozzie with the pointed teeth being allowed to buy up some colour comic from my friend the German Herr Fuhrer, a.k.a. Tiny Whatsisname. This Ozzie fellow has been a staunch supporter of the Boss and little Pillock was frothing at the mouth at the idea of him getting yet another paper in which to rally the faithful. No mention, you may notice, of the fact that all four television channels and most of the wireless is run by paid-up members of the Communist Party and they've also got the support of the fat Czech running the *Daily Mirror* who spends all his time in Moscow.

A propos Tiny Thingummy, I really think I may have to go to that lawyer chap of Munster's after all. Runner-Muck? Farter-Stuck? Not content with smearing the boy Mark and trying to establish links between myself and the Mafia, they've now dragged poor old Charlie Whackett into it. As you may remember, Maurice formed a company called PicTank to buy up army surplus armoured vehicles in Scotland, planning to convert them into Sheikmobile stretched limos for sale in the Middle East. Shortly after the said vehicles had left Southampton, PicTank unfortunately went into liquidation. Meanwhile Charlie's British Used Motors had taken a similar consignment off the M.o.D. in a spirit of patriotic enterprise to relieve them of several car parks full of three-tonners gathering rust on Salisbury Plain. So what, you may well ask. So a sinister conspiracy, according to Herr Fuhrer's Sunday Rag: I am one of Charlie's directors at BUM, therefore there must be a nasty smell in the woodshed. I happen to know that not even the craziest coon banana republic wanted that heap of scrap but anyway Barter-Shmuck will soon wipe the smile from their lips just you see.

I've pencilled the eleventh to get legless at Rye. Give us a bell and I'll ink it in.

See you in court,

DENIS

10 Downing Street

Whitehall

24 JULY 1987

Dear Bill,
I don't know about you, but I've been pretty riveted by this Archer libel case. When I dropped in to the RAC last week for a quick pre-lunch goldfish bowl of the electric soup, conversation in the bar was of very little else. Maurice said he'd come all the way up to town to see the fun and even though he slipped the Clerk of the Court a couple of brown ones before they opened he still found himself at the end of a queue half a mile long. I told him he was well out of it. Can you imagine the smell, Bill? A hundred or so reptiles in their shirt-sleeves and the temperature in the nineties?

What Squiffy Heatherington wanted to know was did he get his end away or didn't he? (They always believe in getting down to brass tacks at the Club.) I said from what I'd seen of Archer all that time he was Number Two to Munster, he looked to me like a randy little creep who wouldn't be too choosy about which drainpipe the rat went up. At this, Barry

16

the Barman pipes up and says why should a chap with all those countless millions of pounds and books all over Gatwick Airport go knocking off an old slag at fifty quid a toss when surely he could have women flown in from Paris, real corkers? Squiffy said there was no accounting for tastes in this field and that some wealthy punters he knew couldn't pass a Leprosy Hospital without wanting to chance their arm. No names, no packdrill, but at the conclusion of his remarks he gave Maurice a very watery look.

Maurice said what a chap did with his wedding tackle was his own concern and things had come to a pretty pass when you couldn't take the dog for a walk without the News of the World hiding under the bed with a tape recorder. I said I held no brief for the tartarino in question, but I thought she'd put her finger on it in no uncertain terms when she tore into little Archer and asked him what the hell he thought he was doing, dragging his missus through all the filth, and went on to castigate those fat cat lawyers for making more money out of it than she was.

One theory advanced by Squiffy's friend Doug was that he'd told his better half his nose was clean and so he had to go through with it all. My own view is that the little creep is loving every minute of it, counting his column inches and thinking about the till at Gatwick Airport.

I must say, I couldn't refrain from reminding the Boss that we had this man using the towel in our downstairs lavatory as recently as last Christmas and didn't she regret having dandled him, as it were, upon her knee? She gave me a frosty look, declined to answer for some minutes and then said on leaving the table that she was surprised I had nothing better to do than pore over smutty newspapers. I forebore to counter that this kind of remark came pretty ill from the lips of one who spent the whole of the last two weeks hounding down that poor senile old fart in Australia. Her latest move is to try and stop Mr Wright from picking up his royalty cheque, which thanks to her efforts will be even bigger than Archer's. She's even gone off to America to try and persuade Hopalong to freeze his account, as if the elderly gunslinger hadn't got enough on his plate as it was trying to remember what it was he said he'd forgotten. Boris says incidentally that Wright lives in a tar-papered shack in the slums of Sydney with the arse hanging out of his trousers, so why not let the poor old sod go out on a few cigars and magnums of champagne when all he's done is to pave the way for the Boss by pulling the rug from under Wilson and the macintosh Johnny?

'. . . *turned out to be old Enoch of all people . . .*'

6.

I thought it was you on the blower very late the other night, ringing to confirm our Muirfield outing, but it turned out to be old Enoch of all people. Would I tell M. that he was very grateful for the offer of a peerage, but there was no question of his taking it unless she upped it to a Hereditary one. I said it was very noble of him to be considering his son and heirs, and that my disinclination to accept the title of Earl of Grantham was based on similar thinking. 'No, no,' keened our moustachioed philosopher. 'You have failed to grasp my point, Mr Thatcher. I have two daughters and no son.' This one stymied me a bit, and I swallowed the contents of my glass to focus the mind. 'Ah,' I replied, whereupon he wished me goodnight and replaced the receiver. Ironic, when you think how sane he is about the things that really matter. Talking of which, Mrs Van der K. was wondering whether you and I would care to 'come on down' as P.W.B. has cracked the whip and got that little Bishop hopping back into his basket.

See you on the first tee.

Yours, eyeballs awash,

DENIS

10 Downing Street
Whitehall

7 AUGUST 1987

Dear Bill,

Thank you for the copy of *Spycatcher*, which your American friend brought in from Los Angeles. I hear from the Major that Maurice shipped over two crates of them labelled Citrus Fruit Perishable and set up a stall on the M25 flogging them to the punters in the traffic jam at £200 a go. Unfortunately there was a cloudburst and most of his stock had to be written off, as did his toupee.

On the same topic, I had a call from Mayhew, the lawyer chappie who's taken over Havers' old job. Could I have a word with the Boss in the peace of the matrimonial chamber? He pointed out that it was a bit ridiculous for teams of expensive colleagues of his to be battling away in hot courtrooms in every corner of the globe, when they could be on holiday? After all the book had come out and anyone could read it. What's more one or two judges had had a word with him at the Garrick to the effect that they were being made to look like a lot of Charlies.

I told him he was wasting his time. Margaret was set on her Queen Canute act and once someone had really got her rag she didn't let up this side of the grave.

Talking of judges being made to look Charlies, what price that old wino in the Archer case? According to a doctor I met at the RAC, the old boy had a fairly heavy lunch to celebrate his impending release from the case, and when he went back into the court the stale air had a chemical effect on him and he went totally bananas. Did you read any of it in the *Telegraph*? He worked himself into a frightful froth about that hard-faced bag Mrs Archer, shouted a lot of stuff about her being a vision of unparalleled loveliness and how could anyone in his right mind want to make love to anyone else in the world (shades of Prosser-Cluff chatting up the Typing Pool at the Office Christmas Party). As for the randy little stoat at the centre of the whole tit-and-bum show I could have told his Honour a thing or two that would have made his wig curl. I won't put anything on paper as you never know these days

19

who's going through your dustbins, so it'll have to wait till our lunch at Worplesdon. (Do you know, the little swine even had the cheek to ask me up to Cambridge for champers to celebrate the triumph of British justice.)

'. . . *champers to celebrate the triumph of British justice* . . .'

M. had to go over last week to be pawed by that oily frog Mitterrand and sign the go-ahead for the Channel Tunnel. She came back, I may say, hopping bloody mad and when I heard the scenario I couldn't blame her. I mean surely the whole point of the tunnel is to be able to get behind the wheel of

20

one's limo in Lamberhurst and keep one's foot flat on the floor all the way to Mother Flack's on the Algarve. No go, says Brother Frog. We drive on the wrong side of the road and everyone would be poisoned by the fumes on the way through. So all cars will be loaded on the railway, loaded off again the other end, drivers and passengers herded into cattle-trucks with special 'safety' devices to lock you in in the event of fire. I said personally I'd rather hop on a ferry. At least you can get plastered in some sort of comfort and watch the water going by.

Talking of water, you probably saw Charlie Whackett's run into a spot of trouble with his Theme Park he got me to open a couple of months back. You remember there was a damn-fool photo of us all draped in oilskins being whirled unexpectedly down the rapids after a couple of large ones? The whole trouble nowadays is letting the proles in on larks of that nature. They pay £2.99 to have the hell scared out of them and then get shirty when Charlie's machinery runs amok and throws them all in the water. You mark my words, the next thing you know that tall German who tried to buy Harrods will be plastering my name all over the front of the *Observer* and demanding a Board of Trade Enquiry into me and my Mafia Associates in the Fairground Industry. I've already had a carpeting from the Boss for lending my name to Charlie's Greasy Spoon Eaterie in Covent Garden. However, as I told her, any man who can get the boy Mark off our hands deserves a hereditary peerage. (All the dirt on Hailsham's in my next.)

Abyssinia

Yours,

Plain Mr Denis

DENIS

BAR SNACKS	
· Electric Soup	1·95
· Cold tongue pie	2·80
· Wallbanger & Mash	2·60
· Vegetarian Irish Stew	3·00
· Montezuma Special	2·95

WELCOME
from Mine Hosts of
THE STOAT & COMPASSES

GREG and FLO
PERKINS

21 AUGUST 1987

Dear Bill,

I expect you saw the photo in the *Telegraph* of Yours Truly being made to look a Charlie on the Trevose Golf Course in front of the reptiles. The Corsicans insist that prior to our token 10-day holiday we have to parade before the 'gentlemen of the press' in the forlorn hope that after that we will be left in peace. (Some hope! I caught a grubby little dirty-mac snooper from the *Sun* lurking outside the Club House last night hoping no doubt to get a shot of me slumped over the bar with a gaggle of fellow winos.)

The idea was for me to be seen holing my putt in one while the Boss obligingly held the flag but not surprisingly with all the reptiles flashing their cameras, not to mention assorted members of the hoi polloi standing round in shorts and gawping, I muffed my shot and landed up a couple of yards beyond the cup. There was a general guffaw at this, cries of 'Good Old Den! He's been on the piss again etc' which I must admit made me feel pretty livid. The Boss I may say was none too pleased either when one of the reptiles started asking her trick questions about sending mine-sweepers to the Gulf implying in typical reptile fashion that there had been some kind of turnaround.

What in fact happened was that Hopalong, who has been getting pretty brassed off in recent weeks what with all this Irangate caper not to mention having to have more sections of his nose cut off, decided to go out with a bang knocking the Ayatollah for six (wasn't there some movie years back about a disgraced old gunslinger who came back out of retirement to rid the town of assorted unshaven mobsters? I forget the title but the scenario in Hoppo's case would seem to be faintly similar).

The only snag was that having dispatched his warships to put the fear of God into Mad Old Matey and his mullahs they discovered that they didn't have any equipment in the armoury to deal with mines. So there was an urgent call to the Boss asking her to show solidarity by getting the Navy's old minesweepers out of mothballs.

22

'. . . some movie years back . . .'

M. of course got very excited, shades of the Falklands etc but was persuaded by the FO woofters that in view of all the fuss when she allowed the Yanks to zap Gaddafi from Brize Norton they should postpone any announcement and then make it look as if our minesweepers were going out to protect British ships – a load of codswallop anyway considering that any swarthy coon or dago can run up the Red Ensign and then claim the protection of the Royal Navy!

We've all been having a good laugh about the Batman/Robin split-up. To think that the Doctor was seriously regarded until about ten minutes ago as the only viable alternative to the Boss. Canny little Robin had quite clearly decided some time ago that in future he was going to wear the black cape and mask and therefore decreed that they should all merge their forces into one (the issue of the leadership to be decided later). Unfortunately for Batman his former colleagues, the fat old wino from Brussels and the woman with the untidy hair, all lined up with Robin, leaving the Doc well and truly screwed. The latest is that he's going to carry on regardless rather like that batty old French Cardinal when the Pope did away with all the Latin. How are the mighty fallen, what?

At present it's non-speaks with the Boss after she found my copy of *Spycatcher* in the loo where I'd inadvertently left it. She really hit the roof, Bill, threatening me with injunctions and God knows what if I didn't put it in the incinerator that very instant. Actually I was very happy to oblige as I was finding it pretty heavy going. Apparently Maurice was moved on by the Old Bill when he set up his bookstall on the hard shoulder of the M5. Now he's advertising it in the *Sunday Sport* free with every £50 item of exotic lingerie.

Did you see that the boy Mark nearly came a cropper when the Concorde burst its tyres? I asked the Boss if she thought the pilot might have foolishly allowed him to take over the controls. Blast of Gamma Rays by way of response.

Yours in the rough,

DENIS

10 Downing Street
Whitehall

18 SEPTEMBER 1987

Dear Bill,

I don't know whether you received my rude postcard from Ballater? In any event I hope Daphne didn't lift the Scotsman's kilt as suggested in the caption. I showed it to the Duke before posting, and he thought it was so amusing he took it off to show the Queen Mother. Apart from that it was the usual grisly ordeal. Dead silence at breakfast, clothes changed every half hour, highland games on the Saturday afternoon (fifty miles each way perched in the back of a ghastly Range Rover with H.M. at the wheel yakking about the gee-gees), dinner for sixty to the accompaniment of strangled cat effects on the highland pipes, church parade next morning with ten SAS snipers to every member of the congregation and one in the pulpit scanning the church all through the sermon.

I hear the Major went to the British Telecom AGM and kicked up a bit of a shindig about the rental

'. . . and one in the pulpit . . .'

charge on his cordless, asking why they'd pulled down the red telephone box on the village green and put up a horrible little plate-glass pissoir. I mentioned this to the Boss, as it struck me as being a straw in the wind if the flagship of her Privatisation Policy was, as it were, running into rough water. I don't know whether it had anything to do with it, but the Chairman resigned the following morning pleading ill-health and decrepitude.

The Boss's major preoccupation at the present is the Gulf. As I told you, the original scenario as agreed with the Pentagon was that the Yanks would blow the whistle and M. should appear initially reluctant, thus scotching the Smellysocks' line about her being Hoppo's Poodle. After a suitable interval, however, she would wade into the fray as Washington's only Staunch Ally in the West, tail wagging and beribboned top-knot aquiver. So far so good. Last minute nautical weddings, shades of the Falklands, two points up on the Mori. (Howe, incidentally, who was off pinching bottoms in sunnier climes while his talkative wife turned a blind eye, was hopping mad when he got back to find that one of his underlings, an ambitious little yuppie called Mellors, had been grabbing all the TV interviews in the Lord Palmerston role.) Things took a marked turn for the worse however when the Eyeties, the Frogs and even the Dutch, who nobody knew even had a navy, started sending fleets of minesweepers, cruisers, corvettes and pocket battleships down there as if there was no tomorrow. Even bearing in mind the six months it apparently takes to get there, it seems our boys will be very lucky if there's room to get through the Straits of Hormuz. It'll be just like the Serpentine on a Saturday afternoon. Anyway, according to Boris, the Ayatollah's Saatchis have told him to keep his hair on and extend the hand of reconciliation to the Infidel before the bottom falls out of the oil market. There's even talk he may let out that sidekick of Runcie's with the beard, which seems a pity. But there we are, you win some, you lose some.

The only really good laughs we've had the whole miserable summer came from poor old Batman parting brass rags with little Robin. They've got a new man in now called Macintosh who looks like a prize Charlie. Robin is over the moon as he hated Batman all the time and particularly disliked having to sit on his lap and move his mouth every time he wanted to do his ventriloquist act. The very rum thing is that the

26

Supermarket Johnny, Sainsbury, is going to go on pouring his millions into the Batman Breakaway Group (himself and that very noisy slag from Greenwich). I had a serious word with the Boss while she was cleaning her teeth the other night on the topic: here's the grubby little grocer who's made a fortune out of her new First Come First Served Britain, and he gives it all away to this psychotic struck-off doctor, who has pledged himself to encompass her downfall. Any gongs for the grocery trade, I surmise, will in future go to Marks and Sparks.

Maurice and his Air Malta lady had a pretty disgusting night out in Bath, I gather. Some black-market spiv flogged him a pair of front stalls for £250 to see little Archer's so-called play. He couldn't hear a word for the sound of seats banging and his view was constantly obscured by people getting up to leave, but from what he gathered it was on a level with Prosser-Cluff's Saturday Night Charades in Kuala Lumpur when his queer brother used to dress up as Queen Victoria and do conjuring tricks. Let's hope it will teach the little greaser that even with the weather emanating from his rectum there are cloudy periods.

Are you coming to Blackpool by any chance? There's a form to fill in, which includes the names of all grandparents, together with their religious affiliation, and you won't be able to go for a pee without being frisked on the way in and out. So I'd on the whole disadvise.

Yours aye-atollah,

DENIS

10 Downing Street
Whitehall

Dear Bill,

Autumnal gales have been howling through our little home this week. Ever since the boy Mark announced that he was looking for a million pound-plus Mayfair mansion from which to relaunch his UK Operation, Margaret has been distinctly tetchy and liable to fly off the handle at the least provocation. You may have seen her on the TV savaging the reptiles in her Inner City Whistlestop train.

If you ask me, the whole thing was a bit of a farce. As per usual the Boys in Blue refused to allow any advance publicity about her itinerary for fear of the Bog-trotters, so any hope of flag-wagging piccaninnies emerging from their hovels to greet her a la Duke of Windsor – 'Something must be done' – were well and truly screwed from the outset. Instead we all left in the McAlpines' executive jet with sticking plaster over the windows, and came down in some insalubrious waste Somewhere In The Midlands, where surprise surprise thousands of reptiles were waiting with cameras, TV lights, earphones and things on sticks to record the Boss's tryst with the Other Britain.

Boss then offered a brief walkabout amidst the weeds and World War Two bomb damage, while the cameras whirred and she expressed deep feelings of care and concern.

Then came question time, and some uppity little ragamuffin (from the BBC needless to say) dared to suggest that she herself might be in some way to blame for the scenes of dereliction that lay before us. Krakatoa. Why did he think the Government had any more money than he had? If he was so clever, why didn't he pay some people to build skyscrapers and a shopping centre? By the end of it, I must say, the little bugger looked pretty well hammered into the mud and we moved off to inspect the 'model house' brought up on a low loader from the Daily Mail Ideal Home Exhibition 1981.

As if she wasn't cross enough already, the bearded hooligans in the Gulf had the cheek to row one of their boats within catapult shot of a wog tanker rechristened the *Morning Cloud*

'. . . *Queen Elizabeth defying the Might of Spain . . .*'

in order to annoy them, and had a go with a pea-shooter. Cue for second eruption of aforementioned volcano. Queen Elizabeth defying the Might of Spain. How dare these pirates interfere with honest British merchantmen going about their business in great waters? Preparations were soon to be underway to singe the Ayatollah's beard, forsooth. I thought it my duty to point out that the jolly tars in question were a few Jap chancers on the make with the usual deck cargo of pot-crazed dusky layabouts, and anyway where was HMS *Armadillo* that was supposed to be keeping the Ayatollah's Boy Scouts at bay? I need hardly say that I might just as well have saved my breath to cool the electric soup.

For once I found myself agreeing with Maurice when he rang lateish the other evening about Monsieur le Pen being turned away by Munster. Alfie Sherman, who used to lick stamps for the Boss and toss in the occasional bon mot when Sir Custardface was having trouble with her scripts, is a nice little chap in my view, a former Leftie who saw the light. He told me that this le Pen cove is very sound on all the basic points, and is trying to crack down on the Reds. Of course he sometimes shoots his mouth off about how the crinkly-haired brigade ought to shuffle off back to Tunis, but as Alfie says the Frogs have always been very excitable. Maurice, as far as I could understand, was saying it was a crying shame not to have him on the platform at Blackpool, and he might knock a bit of sense into the likes of Kenneth Baker. Baker, as you may have seen, has been smarming his way round the US of A, trying to pick up a few tips on how to keep punks at school for another couple of years when they could be usefully unemployed. Now he's dragging his feet about privatising education, and if you ask me may well be the next one to walk the plank into the piranha pool.

If you insist on coming to Blackpool I would suggest you put up at the Lytham St Anne's International Hydro Park Hotel, which is adjacent to the Golf Course, run by a very nice little German masseur and his Filipino wife. I have reserved the English Rose Suite in the name of Mr Worsthorne. Give us a bell one way or the other.

Yours under the volcano,

DENIS

10 Downing Street
Whitehall

16 OCTOBER 1987

Dear Bill,

I hope the ambulance journey wasn't too painful, and that the Cottage Hospital is reasonably comfortable. I sent a couple of dozen Lafite to the Matron and hope you will enjoy it as soon as you cease to be Nil by Mouth.

I have carried out extensive investigations at this end and still can't fathom what happened. My usual security man, Wendell, who knows the course like the back of his hand, was laid up with 'flu, and was replaced at the last minute by some dumbo from the SAS Landing Craft *Hesperus* moored offshore throughout the Conference. When he saw you emerging from the copse after your pee I can only think that he mistook you for a homosexual psychopath about to assault me and loosed off in trigger-happy mood with his anti-personnel bazooka. If I were you I'd sue him for every penny you can get out of him, and I've warned Hurd that he can expect no mercy.

What a creep that man is. The whole conference voted loud and clear to bring back the rope. The Boss is in favour of it. I'm in favour of it. It's perfectly obvious to any sane and sensible person that the only possible way to put a stop to all these muggers, glue-sniffers and such is to hang a brace or two on the hour every hour until they pull their socks up. In the face of that, all the prat Hurd can propose is a general amnesty for nail files and corkscrews. Next thing you know, golf clubs will be classified as an offensive weapon.

Munster got very weepy at his farewell Wine and Cheese and made a little speech, saying he bore no grudge against anyone, least of all the Boss, but having served the Party for several years both loyally and selflessly, he was leaving to pursue a career in the City. When he repeated that he bore no grudge against anyone, particularly not the Boss, I noticed M. beginning to inflate the poison ducts and moments later she moved in to present him with a signed photograph of herself in a silver frame.

'. . . moved in to present him with a signed photograph of herself . . .'

The salt was rubbed in the wound when the following day Smarmy C., looking more than ever like a smart undertaker's mute, strode onto the platform to tumultuous applause, though quite what for I had some trouble in deciding. Was it, as Maurice suggested, for getting his end away with Miss K. or, as I myself inclined to think, for being caught with his trousers down and then getting away with it? Whatever the truth, the Boss was in raptures, clapping away like she does at the Opera when Von Karavan comes on to take his bouquet of flowers. I could see the reptiles attempting to focus their long lenses on D.T. failing to share in the general euphoria, but I wasn't born yesterday and grinned like a monkey, applauding with the best of them.

Talking of monkeys, the Boss's new flavour of the month in besuited baboons is the Health Minister, who looks like a cross between a bent American evangelist and that accountant who runs your Rotary in Folkestone. Raeburn? Pringle? No matter. Little Moore is being employed to stick his head over the parapet with various bright ideas, which include handing the National Health Service over to BUPA, punitive charges for dying in hospital, and a phased release of the long-term chronic sick into the community. A lot of it very sound, entre nous, but the Boss has shot her mouth off in the past about her caring and compassion, and I think she may have painted herself into a corner pro tem.

As usual I had to sit up all night watching that ghastly buffoon with the cigarette holder and quilted dressing gown, Sir Custardface, trying to think up a few new gags to liven up M's closing number. Not but what if she read out the Room Service Menu and What To Do In Case Of A Fire those chimpanzees wouldn't all throw their knickers in the air and scream for more.

Our Cousins across the sea seem to be experiencing some trouble in selecting a suitable replacement for the Old Gunslinger. You'd think in a country as large as that they might be able to rustle up someone vaguely presentable who hadn't during the last six months been caught (a) in bed with a tartarino, (b) with his hand in the till or (c) lifting chunks of Pillock's Joke Book for inclusion in his speeches. Not, apparently, so. When I mentioned it over a snort at Claridge's to the boy Mark, who is here house-hunting again, I couldn't help noticing a nasty gleam come into his contact lenses. I imagine his train of thought led from his own clean-cut appearance and famous name, via glamorous blonde wife and Burgerdorfer's millions, to the White House. If so, I would be the last to stand in his way. Anything to ensure his speedy return to the Home of the Brave and the Land of the Free.

Ring me from the hospital as soon as your arm is out of plaster.

Yours in the bloom of health,

DENIS

10 Downing Street
Whitehall

30 OCTOBER 1987

Dear Bill,

You'll forgive me if I sounded a little bewildered on the phone last night but I think I must have been slightly jet-lagged. A man I met in Texas swore blind that if you drank your body weight in spirits on the flight over it was a sure-fire way to avoid any fatigue. As it was, I was comatose throughout the flight, and rang the Lawsons' bell three times between the hours of two and six a.m. asking if I could come into the cockpit and see the controls.

The Boss enjoyed herself no end at the Commonwealth get-together in Toronto. The Coons, headed by Mr Eeba Gum, kicked off stroppy as hell, berating her for giving comfort to P.W.B. and branding her as a narrow-minded materialist only interested in money. In the old days, M. could have counted on the Dominions to rally behind the Mother Country against the massed ranks of Hottentots. But nowadays you get a pretty queer class of character running these places. The Canadian, Muldoon, is an absolute stumblebum who has to have his trousers labelled front and back so he doesn't wet himself, and the King of the Ozzies is a stringy ex-convict Leftie called Buzzard, a Pillock of the Outback. Neither of them has any respect for the Boss.

Not that she gave a monkey's, forty-nine against one being her idea of a fun party. She tore strips off Eeba Gum, accusing him of taking the White Man's shilling and then kicking him in the groin, not to mention doing numerous shifty deals with P.W.B. without whose funding Zimbanana would be down the pan. Muldoon got pretty short shrift as well when she revealed courtesy of MI5 that the Canadians' graph of trade with Brother Boer looked like a fireman's ladder. You should have seen their faces, Bill, when confronted by a strong woman telling the truth. What really put the wind up the Sambos was her announcement that she was thinking of doing a whistle-stop tour of the so-called Front-Line States to check out the malarkey at first hand.

'. . . rang the Lawsons' bell three times between the hours of two and six a.m. . . .'

No wonder we went off on a big high, our hotel room decked out in orchids and knee-deep in bottles of champagne, all specially flown in from Jo'burg by Mrs Van der K. and her Friends of Freedom Fellowship.

Next stop Dallas. As I think I told you, we got a nasty shock a month or so back when the boy Mark suddenly turned up in London, announcing that he was looking for a million-pound mansion in Mayfair from which to relaunch himself on the UK. Margaret seemed unperturbed at the prospect, but you can imagine my own feelings, just when I thought we were shot of the little bugger once and for all. I got on the blower to Charlie Whackett and proposed what I thought was a reasonable deal: i.e. he would pledge to stay put for a minimum period of say five years negotiable and in return we would do him a slap-up full-dress state visit to the Buggerorffs with helicopter security and all the trimmings, thus dramatically raising his profile imagewise as Texas's leading scrapshooter.

I need hardly say it was a tough bargain, specially as I'm not even sure if he won't welsh on it. Pa Burgerstand had laid on a four-day jamboree, jazz band playing by the pool, immense helpings of cow pie, every disgusting variety of American snort ladled out by black women in white gloves, and probably the ghastliest shower of seedy used-car dealers and their grisly reconditioned second wives the world has ever seen, all desperate to press the flesh of Hoppo's Best Friend and Staunchest Ally. Charlie got a bit carried away by it all, insisting on me downing the World's Biggest Chocolate and Coconut Cocktail for the television cameras, then trying to push me into the pool in my tuxedo and studs. I don't mind telling you I got pretty brassed off and spent the rest of the evening in a sulk.

Following the hurricane, Maurice tells me he has been out with his chainsaw at Scotney 'on our behalf' securing various exotic veneers for sale on the Japanese market. He thought he'd got hold of an Ougadouga Spruce, the only one of its kind in the world, highly prized for inlaid dashboards in customised limos but by the time he'd hired Pickfords from Tunbridge Wells to drive it roots and all to Harwich on two hundred-foot trailers, a man at the dock gates pointed out that it was a diseased elm and not worth tuppence. Not that one should laugh at Maurice's enterprise, though it is a great relief to have got rid of all those soggy old trees that litter the place up every autumn, getting in the way of planning applications and often hindering the development of golf courses.

Perhaps we should meet to drown our sorrows at having all those points wiped off us during the past few days. I personally blame Matey next door for going on the box and telling everyone not to panic. One sight of Nigel shaking his double chins about and telling the City that everything was ticketyboo was enough to send them plunging off the ledges like lemmings. Anyway, the joke is that they've told him in no uncertain terms what he can do with his BP Offer and I scattered a few prospectuses on his doorstep when I got back from the Club after lunch in order to rub his nose in it.

See you at the Rotary. Remind me of the name of the little man in the toupee I mistook for Bob Monkhouse last year. Or was it him? Not that it matters.

Yours in the Snug,

DENIS

13 NOVEMBER 1987

Dear Bill,

I don't know whether you're up to date with the Maurice saga, but the last I heard he was under sedation at the clinic for rich winoes near Hove that he escaped from last year. It all started, I gather, when his Bank Manager rang on Settlement Day to draw attention to his portfolio, which far from being a Blue Chip affair in the first place, had been entirely financed by a loan, the security for which included three houses in Tonbridge of which Maurice did not appear to be the owner, a used Jaguar car obtained under a hire purchase agreement, and a flat in Deal, the leasehold of which was owned by a Mrs Bernadette Mifsud, a former employee of Air Malta. They were now calling this loan in, the portfolio itself being in a minus situation, and would welcome a cheque for £1.5 million at his earliest convenience.

'. . . *staggered to a ground floor window . . . and jumped . . .*'

According to the Major, Maurice then went to Lingfield Races where he put his remaining assets on a horse called Belly Dancer, which had a heart attack as the tapes went up, seriously injuring its jockey. He then adjourned to the Dog and Trumpet in Burgess Hill where he fell in with a crowd of former Double Glazing colleagues who were also drowning their sorrows on tick, staggered to a ground floor window on the pretence of going to the lavatory and jumped. He was found some hours later, unconscious in the car park.

The Boss has been taking it equally badly. There she was at Blackpool, crest of the economic wave, all her policies vindicated with production at an all-time high, knocking the Japs for six on the growth front, and now the brokers' men are in. You should have heard her the other night on the subject of Hoppo. It was hard to imagine that only a short time ago he was Flavour of the Month, the Saviour of the Western World, the Only Man Who Understood Her. 'Look at him,' she exploded, pointing to a picture in that new newspaper with the big lettering, 'he should be in a home for derelicts. How could a senile wreck like that be seen as a source of confidence, incapable as he is of making the simplest decisions, even about personal hygiene? Whatever made them think a former film star could guide the destinies of a great nation?'

I was inwardly gratified to see the old girl had come round to my point of view of the Cowboy, albeit somewhat late in the day. I have found by experience however that it is unwise to crow on such occasions and was particularly glad when Fatty from next door got the full weight of it in the neck.

Even prior to the so-called volatility of the Stock Market, Margaret's nerves had been severely frayed by the Lord Young Fiasco. You probably remember Young, or more probably you don't. He's one of these brown-tonguers in a suit who can be seen hovering about the Conferences and is put on the telly from time to time to explain away the Unemployment Figures. Personally I never liked the cut of his jib, and according to that broker friend of the Major's, Fearnley-Whittingstall, there was a slight whiff of smelly fish about his property business in Finchley. The Boss, however, was head over heels. 'He gets things done,' she used to say, 'while the rest of you sit around chewing the fat.' Old Oyster-Eyes, who someone I met at the Club the other night almost convinced me was dead, is in fact still looming in the shadows, and he came down very heavily against the Finchley Wide-Boy becoming Chairman of the Party on the grounds that extracting mammoth contributions from Fat Cats in the City would ill accord with an even-handed policy as Minister for Employment. The Boss threw a fit, her will would prevail, Whitelaw could get back to the Lake District and shoot his pheasants till he was blue in the face, the days were gone when the fate of the Tory Party was decided over the polished mahogany at country house weekends.

Meanwhile, however, Twinkletoes himself, seeing that he was being passed the Poisoned Cocoa, prudently declined. Munster had the last laugh as she had to swallow her rage and ask him to stay on until a suitable stumblebum turned up in the person of some old buffer called Brooke who I am told used to be at the Home Office in the Macmillan days.

Our only social event as the storm clouds gathered was a farewell champagne buffet for the Corsican Twins, who have been given the heave-ho as part of the Munster New Broom. Both Alberto and Luigi got very weepy, as one would expect, and buttonholed me individually to say that my wife was a hard and heartless woman who cast men aside like used Kleenexes. It is a song with which I am very familiar, though I have never heard it before in that quaint Italian accent. But I have never liked them as a race after their fighting style in the Last Show, so I told the twins that I was not going to stand there and hear my wife insulted by a couple of Eyeties. The new man, who oddly enough used to work for them, is a plump and somewhat restless operator called Bell, who I think must suffer from some sort of bladder trouble as he is for ever vanishing into the Gents and coming out blowing his nose.

I thought we might go and visit Maurice. I could drive you down in the Roller, and we could have lunch at the Crooked Billet.

Yours in the red,

DENIS

39

10 Downing Street
Whitehall

Dear Bill,

Did you spot me on TV at the Mansion House making gallant conversation to Mrs Horace Puckle of the Westminster Ladies Inner Wheel? Crikey, what a snorer! The woman on the other side was apparently Mother Runcie, which I didn't discover until after it was all over, otherwise I'd have given her a piece of my mind about Poofs in the Pulpit as the *Sun* so wittily dubbed them. Thank God Archie Wellbeloved has turned his toes up. It would have finished him off to see his beloved C of E taken over by the shirtlifters. Snaggleteeth Runcie, who said the grace in his usual pansified tones, has proved quite incapable of smoking them out, and if I were you I'd watch that new skypilot of yours like a hawk. I saw him mincing about at Maurice's Car Boot Sale with an armful of lampshades and the look on his face when he thanked the policeman at the gate would have curdled the milk.

When it came to the Boss's turn to speak, she delivered a stern lecture to Hoppo, telling him to take a leaf out of her book. It may have been the Rotary Woman and the booze – they always serve very fancy French plonk on these occasions – but I couldn't for the life of me understand what Margaret was talking about. She kept saying that Hopalong must take his courage in both hands etc etc, but if she meant he was to put up his taxes why does Matey next door keep taking ours down, and if she meant make cuts in the National Health Service they haven't got one. I asked Furniss about it yesterday and he was completely baffled. His view is that things are perfectly all right as long as you don't need the money, and he kept saying, 'Anyway, it's only paper,' as he refilled my schooner with his Lebanese Amontillado. I said it wasn't paper as far as I was concerned, it was years of wearing my arse out on the Board at Burmah, and he'd better pull his finger out or I'd be transferring my overdraft to the Hong Kong Midland Bank.

The Smellysocks did their best to try and make capital out

'. . . as he refilled my schooner with his Lebanese
Amontillado . . .'

of the Underground Fire which I thought was really kicking
below the belt, especially when the Boss had done her Florence
Nightingale and been filmed by the media bringing words
of comfort to the Emergency Services. One jumped-up little
Labour Johnny in a beard had the effrontery to blame the
Boss's Privatisation Policy for the fact that there were no beds
in the hospital the victims were first taken to, adding that the
fire would never have started if the cleaning staff had not been
reduced to two coons with a mop. I ask you, Bill. Surely there
are times when Party Politics should be put to one side, while
the nation stands in silence. They behaved equally badly over
the Irish business. No sooner has the smoke cleared than
Friend of the Gays Red Ken is up on his soap box, telling us
we should get out of Ireland and leave them to cut their own
throats in peace. Always my own view, entre nous, but again
there is a time and place, as Gingernuts Pillock clearly felt
when he scragged Livingstone for having buggered up his own
publicity stunt choppering over to Dublin to shake hands with
that little spiv Haughey.

41

Talking of spivs, I saw that arch-greaser Baker coming out of the Boss's den the other morning, for once in his life with his hair somewhat awry. 'That woman!' I heard him muttering to himself as he cleaned his hornrims on his shirt-tail. He confided in me, I think as a fellow-victim, that Margaret has got completely carried away with some wild-cat scheme to bring back Greyfriars and Mr Chips, all the parents being expected to rise up and 'vote themselves out of the system' paving the way for bills of four or five thou. a year for each of their little ones. According to Baker, the Boss is in a minority of one, but as usual that only strengthens her resolve. 'Poor old Tebbit,' he moaned, 'now I see why he wanted to opt out.'

I gather, on a brighter note, that Smarmy Cecil is well and truly up shit creek with the Electric Light Company. His latest wheeze is to unhook the power stations from the National Grid and sell them off to the Japs, which even I, Bill, in my inebriated dotage, brain cells flooding through the sieve like wet spaghetti, can see is a non-starter. I understand his days are numbered, which will no doubt delight little Miss Keays, always waiting to perform a fandango on his grave.

What are your Christmas plans? The Burgerstands have invited us over for a special Yuletide Hoe-Down by the pool, scheduled to go on for two days with every mug in Texas who's bought a heap of their motorway scrap in '87 on hand to press the flesh. The Boss seems vaguely tempted, if only as an inducement to the little sod to stay away for another few months. But I pointed out that the Texan climate is notoriously fickle and that we could well be swept away in a hurricane and end up Somewhere Over the Rainbow. Talking of Mark reminds me of that disgusting Branson flogging his rubber johnnies on the BBC. Even the Boss failed to come to his defence when I cast aspersions on his appointment as Mr Cleanup.

From one of your old Mates,

DENIS

10 Downing Street
Whitehall

Dear Bill,

Maurice rang me from the Home last night, very low. He'd been pinning all his hopes on Picmail, the Private Enterprise answer to the GPO, with his Pakistanis delivering Christmas cards at a tenner a throw, and had even bussed several in from Belgium in very cramped conditions under the floor of a minivan, when the strike was cancelled. I was pretty cheesed off as well, as I'd been hoping to be excused boots altogether on the Christmas card front and will now have to sign four and a half thousand of those damnfool Number Ten specials with the two of us grinning like a pair of chimpanzees on the front step.

Hopalong was pretty livid with M. for agreeing to participate in the Refuelling Stopover Microsummit with Gorbo at Brize Norton, which he felt was an attempt to upstage his Grand Finale Walkdown number with Mr Glasnost, the new smiling face of the Evil Empire. The old boy actually managed to get on the blower, warning her against being duped by the Moscow Saatchis. As I could have told him, he would have done better to save his breath for other purposes. 'Now listen to me, Ronald, for one moment,' I heard her steely voice insist, 'Mr Gorbachov and I have forged a very special friendship, a friendship I value and cherish. Unlike you, I have been to Russia and have seen the wonderful way in which simple Muscovites can take a Western leader to their hearts.' I could hear the grinding of dentures across the ether, but she persisted. 'After our time together in Georgia, it is hardly surprising that Mr Gorbachov would want to see me first, to hear the views of the Western Alliance from an active and decisive mind and one moreover who is going to be there for many, many years to come.' With this she firmly replaced the receiver, remarking that the President was a spent force, even as an actor, let alone as a human being.

As a matter of fact, all this stuff about her being Wonderwoman and still able to go twenty rounds with King Kong is not a hundred percent true. For some time now, the old girl has been complaining of mysterious twinges in the upper vertebrae and even went so far as to invest a couple of hundred guineas in calling out Dr O'Gooley. The old wino came round on Saturday afternoon looking pretty flushed, made a cursory examination in the Cabinet Room and took me into the den for a quiet word: 'Pain in the neck,' he murmured as I offered to top him up. 'You don't have to tell me, chummo,' I riposted, 'and you haven't got to live with her.' It transpired however that he was diagnosing a medical condition often associated with overwork. There was nothing to be done about it except for prolonged rest. Fat chance of that, I said.

The same evening we dropped into Buck House for some Royal Cheese and Wine Occasion and Margaret made the mistake of accepting one of the Queen Mother's 'Piledrivers' and fell to the floor. While the Royals were trying to bring her round on a spare bed, she confided in H.M. that her neck had been giving her trouble, with the result that the ancient Van der Pump was dug out of the Doubles Bar at the Ritz for an

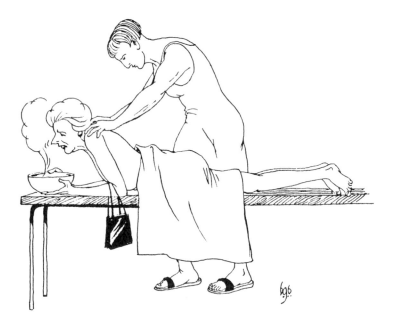

'. . . a crop-headed Amazon in Hampstead who makes her lie on a plank . . .'

Alternative Consultation. Apparently the Queen is frightfully keen on all this herbal stuff and before M. knew where she was she was referred to a crop-headed Amazon in Hampstead who makes her lie on a plank and inhale parsley fumes, which Margaret swears is doing her the world of good.

So to our historic tryst with the Evil Emperor and his Consort. Margaret got very excited as we were driving down the M40. 'What is happening today, Denis, marks a turning point in the history of Western Civilisation. From this morning there is a shift in the balance of power.' I said I'd drink to that. When we arrived at Brize Norton, the place was swarming with SAS bouncers, police armed to the teeth, and three or four thousand well-drilled reptiles from all over the world. 'There you are, dear,' M. observed as we left the limo in a storm of flashlights, 'dear Mr Gorbachov will have a little glimpse of the free world.' It transpired that my role was to mind the Missus while the Big Two settled the problems of the globe in a nearby hangar. Not a snort in sight, Mrs G. complete with a moustachioed lady interpreter, both as you can imagine pretty heavy going. 'Russian people so interested in your National Health Service. I am most intrigued to learn what percentage of the Government Income is spent on this', was her opening googly. I must have looked a bit blank, and after a moment or two the interpreter said something to her in Russian with a very straight face that made Mrs G. roar with laughter. To fill the ensuing silence I explained that we were quite near Huntercombe, but she seemed to have very little interest in golf. After what seemed an age, the two World Leaders emerged to nod and smile for the cameras, and I was able to slip away to the RAF Mess for a Megasnort with the Wincos.

Did you get an invitation on a card shaped like a bottle with spangles stuck all over it? It turns out to be a surprise party for the Major's seventy-fifth given by a bunch of former ATS officers in Tonbridge. It could be quite a jolly do, an opportunity to ease ourselves into the Festive Season. Why don't I pick you up at the Club and we can motor down? You'll have to drive on the way back, as I intend to get thoroughly pickled.

Dosvidanya,

DENIS

10 Downing Street
Whitehall

25 DECEMBER 1987

Dear Bill,

I gather I have you to thank for taking away my keys to the Roller during the final stages of the Major's Beano at Tonbridge. I have a clear recollection of trying to do my Gorilla in the grand piano and the lid coming down on my head but after that everything went blank. Did we sing carols outside the Police Station or was that a dream? The Major's wife seemed pretty surprised to find me behind the sofa the following afternoon. The old boy had scarpered knowing there would be only cold tongue pie in the larder, so I got a double helping.

Probably just as well I didn't take to the road after what happened to Mrs Matey next door. You must have seen the headlines about her prang. The Boss got very shirty. 'It really is too much, Denis,' she complained over her breakfast capsule of Vitamin C, 'just when we're trying to crack down once and for all on the menace of the drunken driver, one does expect those in high places to set an example.' Personally, for once in a pretty frosty relationship, I felt rather sorry for Mrs Matey and wrote her a note of sympathy. All the reptiles were baying for her blood, no experience of that sort of thing, very timid by nature, and, as I said to her, being married to a politician I wouldn't blame her if she sought occasional solace in the cocktail cabinet. Even Lawson himself seemed to see the sense of my note and was emboldened to smite the reptiles hip and thigh, accusing them of hounding a poor defenceless woman who had done nothing wrong. It was just her bad luck that some irresponsible monkey of a busdriver had recognised her and reversed his bus into her parked car while she was doing the *Daily Telegraph* crossword puzzle.

Talking of people being hounded, I was very sorry for the poor skypilot in Oxford who voiced what we had all long been thinking about Runcie. I was talking to that retired Bishop in the Club with the very red face – Merryweather, Pickering, some name like that – who is always very sound on matters pertaining to the cloth, and his view is that the Shirtlifters are now in absolute control and that this poor old boy was about to blow the gaffe in the *Church Times* and name names. Next thing, four curates from the East End ring his doorbell in the middle of the night and the rest is history. I saw Hurd just after I got back from lunch and said he ought to look into it, but I got the usual sneering condescension and the suggestion that I'd be unwise to go too near a naked flame. That man is so busy refusing a licence to every poor farmer who wants to have a bang at a poacher, no wonder he's got no time for serious business.

Boss got very steamed up when the Round Robin arrived from Harley Street with a lot of fat cats in striped trousers accusing her of running down the NHS. 'How dare they,' she fumed, 'when they know perfectly well that we have spent countless millions of decent people's money on those who are too indolent and short-sighted to join BUPA like the rest of us.' It turned out that her Health Johnny, one of the brown-tongued brigade by the name of Moore, is in the Clinic having ruptured himself in her service, so Mogadon Man, who had nothing much to do nowadays, was wheeled out to deliver a stinging rebuke to the Stethoscope Millionaires as being entirely responsible for the downward drift of the Hospital Service. The fact that they were having to shut up shop and close down all the beds was nothing to do with the Government. It was too many cigars and holidays in the West Indies on the part of the Consultants.

As a result, O'Gooley, who came round to make me pee in a jar for the Scottish Widows, made a point of refusing to warm his hands before proceeding with the examination, and was then unwise enough to tap on the Boss's door afterwards and ask for a donation for the Nurses' Christmas Comfort Fund. I was still putting on my trousers at the time, so I didn't hear the full text of her reply, but he got pretty short shrift. The private sector didn't seem to have any problem paying their nurses, wasn't it time the Health Service introduced Time and Motion like everybody else, cut out the scrimshankers and stopped pouring money down every available drain?

We're still waiting for word from Dallas about the Burger-dorffs' Christmas Schedule. Behind my back the Little Woman rang up Ma Burgerdorff, who as you may recall had suggested a Yuletide Hoe-Down by the Pool, and asked the whole bloody lot of them over to an Old Fashioned British Christmas at

Chequers with the Howes. I think even old Mr Junk Motors himself may have the sense to opt for the Hoe-Down, but Fate can be very cruel, and I live in momentary horror of the telephone call that will announce their acceptance. Wu rang up quite late last night to say that the central heating is on the blink and that there are mushrooms coming out of the ceiling in the Yellow Bedroom where the Donald Sindens usually sleep. Boss is making a list of Black Sheep to be welcomed into the Fold on Boxing Day. Smarmy C. has already accepted, as have the Archers, but fortunately Sir Robert Armstrong and his Cordon Bleu lady have been invited out to Australia for a Wright Case Reunion at Ayer's Rock. Munster, I must say, has sent a very offensive Christmas card of a Snowman with a carrot stuck into it and the inscription inside 'Get stuffed, Norman'.

'. . . O'Gooley, who came round to make me pee
in a jar . . .'

I shall expect the Escape Vehicle to spring me on Boxing Day according to plan and Mine Host at the Waggonload of Monkeys promises us an upstairs room with a roaring fire and as much methylated spirits as we can drink.

Good Yøl,

DENIS

 10 Downing Street
Whitehall

8 JANUARY 1988

Dear Bill,

I'm sorry I couldn't join you in the Cat and Hamster on Sunday morning but Margaret summoned the reptiles to a photo-call to mark her points victory over Asquith as longest-serving Prime Minister ever. What does that make me, you ask? Longest-suffering member of RAC, what? I think I deserve a gong or better still a very large snorterino.

I did enjoy our Boxing afternoon at the Waggonload of Monkeys, though I could have done without Maurice's blue video. I am a broad-minded man, but I found the episode with the lady gorilla and the hairdryer went far beyond the bounds of acceptable adult entertainment, even in our permissive world. I thought at the time that the Major was rather foolhardy to invite the Old Bill up to our private suite to avoid any misunderstandings on the drive home, but I think Boris's Russian dynamite had got to him by the time the gorilla came on.

The news on Old Oyster-Eyes is that he's out of the wood, but the medics have told him that he's going to have to go very gently on the snort front in future. I popped in to see him in the Westminster when he was still feeling a bit peaky and had my Get Well Present roughly snatched out of my hands by a giant blackamoor in a white coat as if I was some kind of pusher. At that stage poor old Willie was still pretty weepy saying it was the end of the road, and if he hadn't done the

49

decent thing by that prat Heath he could have been Prime Minister. I pointed out that he wouldn't have enjoyed it, think of the misery he'd spared poor old Lady Whitelaw, and that he still had many good years ahead as the Boss's ADC. At this he burst into tears and began banging his head against the wall so I was told by one of the nurses that I was upsetting the patient and must leave. I understand that M. went in later in the day and told him that the best tonic he could give himself and the country would be to get out of bed and go to work on his red boxes a.s.a.p.

'. . . I popped in to see him in the Westminster . . .'

Any hope that the Boss would put her feet up over the Festive Tide was dashed at dinner on New Year's Eve when I was down in the cellar dusting off some Very Old Crusty Port-Style Wine laid down by Bonar Law with which to see in the New Year. Margaret suddenly appeared at the head of the cellar steps, the expression on her face indicating that celebration was not in order. 'Leave Mr Wu to do that, Denis. This is important. Go and answer the front door. I think it is the Attorney General.' Sure enough there on the step was some bird in striped trousers who turned out to have drawn the short straw in the Havers Handicap, name of Mayhew. I took him through into the Baldwin Room, where Margaret was pretending to read the *Daily Telegraph*. 'Happy New Year, Prime Minister!' he began. 'I have with me the new subpoenas and necessary writs relating to the Wright Case. Nevertheless –' he continued, opening a large attache case and producing various documents bound in red tape – 'I feel it my duty as your legal adviser to ask you to consider very carefully whether the game is worth the candle. Recourse to the Court of Appeal will only incur additional expense, and with so much of the material already in the public domain, we must ask ourselves whether any useful purpose can now be served by further litigation.'

Having had some experience of lawyers at Burmah, I looked pretty canny as I offered him a mug of Gluhwein. It was pretty obvious to me that he didn't fancy the idea of burning the midnight oil through the cold months of the year and preferred to take the money and run for it. However the Boss, who had been drumming her fingers impatiently on the arm of her chair, quickly put an end to his dreams of a prolonged Winter-break in the Seychelles. 'Now listen to me, Mayhew. There is an important issue at stake here. Either we have a Secret Service or we don't.' 'But Prime Minister,' Mayhew foolishly interposed, 'the Judge in the case has ruled in his wisdom that maintaining a total cloak of secrecy is impossible this side of the Iron Curtain . . .' At this my wife's eyes flashed and a flush mantled her cheek. 'Wisdom fiddlesticks! I will not be lectured on how to run this country. See to it that when the case comes to appeal the judges are men of sounder perception as to where the national interest lies. I would suggest Lord Hailsham is recalled to hear the case. He could always be relied upon to be impartial in a matter of this kind.'

From the set of Mayhew's mouth I could tell that he was even then mentally ringing his travel agent to cancel the package. As I was showing him to the door he said it was sad how some once great families had destroyed themselves by a passion for litigation. Estates dispersed. Children reduced to penury. Could I not have a word in the shell-like at a suitable moment? Sometimes a loved one could succeed where others failed. I said bollocks to that and if I was in his boots I'd cancel the summer holiday as well.

51

Anyway I must post this quickly as we're off now on our so-called Front Line winter break in Coonland. Luckily I'm glad to say most of our fuzzy-headed friends have given M. the thumbs down pleading other more pressing engagements.

Yours in the cooking pot,

DENIS

10 Downing Street
Whitehall

22 JANUARY 1988

Dear Bill,

I still haven't recovered from my stint among the Coons. Apart from a nasty dose of Montezuma's Revenge brought on by eating boiled snails in Lagos I still wake up sweating several times during the night from dreams in which I am buried under a heap of bare-breasted tribal dancers. Still, I suppose it was all worthwhile if it helped P.W.B. The trouble is I'm not sure whether it did. According to Mrs Van der Kafferbescher, who was on the blower within minutes of our touching down, some people over there are now going round saying that the Boss is a dangerous Left-winger altogether too friendly with Gorbachov and no doubt up to something with the Front Liners.

Poor old Oyster-Eyes had his bed finally shunted out through the door last week as you probably saw. Loyal as ever, the old boy had rung from Intensive Care, saying he was keen to soldier on, even if it meant dying in harness. The medics had told him apparently that another few weeks with the Boss was a death warrant, but he was game, bless his embroidered evening slippers. However Cecilia, with whom I have found myself trapped on the sofa from time to time, read the riot act and told him that he must choose between love and duty or he would feel the sharp end of her shooting stick.

I was present at the somewhat maudlin scene that ensued hard on this ultimatum. The old laird, eyes brimming with tears, twisting his deerstalker in his hands, declined on medical advice my offer of a nip of Highland Fling Japanese Whisky to steady his nerves, and embarked on a broken monologue. 'Something I have to say, Margaret, which will be painful for both of us. God knows, we have weathered many storms together . . .' At this the Boss looked up from the report she was reading, and fixed him with a gimlet eye. 'I am a busy woman, Willie, so please come to the point.' 'I am sorry. I am so sorry. It is a distressing piece of news that I have to break. Bear with me, Prime Minister, while I find the words to express what is in my heart.'

I could see that this was going down like a cup of cold sick with my little woman. 'If you are about to tell me that you wish to retire, that comes as no surprise to me, having read the doctors' report. Government today cannot be carried on by the infirm, let alone the amateur gentleman in plus fours, as once it was.' Huge tears now began to pour down the old boy's cheeks. 'To think,' he sobbed, 'that I sacrificed my career, my hopes of high office, so that you could run ahead and win the prize.' 'Pull yourself together, Willie,' snapped the Boss. 'You know perfectly well that the Party would have got nowhere under your leadership. Could you have taken on Scargill as I did? Crushed the might of Argentina? Won three consecutive elections? Ha! Why, you are incapable even of picking up a twelve bore without shooting your best friend in the leg.' She then, in a way I have often noticed in the fairer sex, changed tack with great suddenness, and rising from her desk, laid a hand on the old gentleman's trembling shoulder.

'How can you desert me like this?' she soothed. 'Now when we most need you. You were so skilled, so irreplaceable. Very well then, leave me in the lurch, abandon me, go back to your grouse moor, but don't think I shall ever be consolable!'

After he had gone, she got on the blower pronto to every conceivable geezer with a handle to his name who had ever voted Conservative, even that fuzzy-haired weirdo art-dealer called Gowrie who left because he couldn't make ends meet on thirty thou. a year. Just before midnight she finally managed to bag some poor old bugger called Bedstead who had clearly had a few and thought at first it was a practical joke. He didn't realise what had hit him until it was too late.

Poor little Steel seems to have cooked his goose. Personally I blame the wife. (He's already been under observation several times by the men in white coats, I gather.) First of all he picks

'. . . the Doctor, who is pushed over
the Reichenbach Falls . . .'

a fight to the death with his old friend the Doctor, who is pushed over the Reichenbach Falls to general hilarity, all in the cause of union. However Steel clearly hadn't reckoned with Macwhatsisname the Scottish lawyer who stepped into the Doctor's surgical boots. Do you remember the meeting we had at Burmah with that accountant man which went on all night? As I recall we went in after a decent dinner convinced we'd got it sewn up. But old Four-Eyes droned on and on about 'above and below the line' and 'writing off loans' and was generally so paralysingly boring that by four in the morning we agreed to everything he asked for. Exactly the same with Steel. Staggered out into the darkness before dawn only to find that he'd signed his name to increasing VAT, ending mortgage relief and declaring war on the Russkies. Of course the woolly-headed Liberals snatched it off the presses, went bananas and now the Wee Laird seems likely to be released into the community. Stand by for the Doctor's comeback and a prize joke that'll be.

Did you see the Boss's very amusing New Year's prank at the expense of Runcie? She decided to make the Chief Rabbi a Duke, putting him on a par with Snaggleteeth in the House of Lords. Entre nous, he's a very sound chap who doesn't go along with this Left-wing nancy boy stuff and thinks they should be strung up. He also says a woman's place is in the home, but I don't know how the Boss squares that with her own manner of carrying on. A propos, do congratulate Maurice on 'stinging' the Archbish for twelve grand to spring Waite. It made Margaret laugh for some minutes.

Yours to the end of the road,

DENIS

BAR SNACKS	
. Electric Soup	1·95
. Cold tongue pie	2·80
. Wallbanger & Mash	2·60
. Vegetarian Irish Stew	3·00
. Montezuma Special	2·95

WELCOME
from Mine Hosts of
THE STOAT & COMPASSES

GREG and FLO
PERKINS

Dear Bill,

I'm amazed you stayed awake for the Boss's *Panorama* live from Downing Street with Mr Teddy-Bear Dimbleby. I used to quite enjoy these occasions when they had that old wino with the specs and the bow-tie. I would take him up to the Den beforehand and get him absolutely wrecked on the electric soup, thus ensuring that the Boss would run rings round him when they got on the air. It was all very agreeable. However when I tried the same technique on young Dimbleby he got very snooty at my expense, saying that some of us had work to do but that he wouldn't say no to a glass of Chateau Montrose after the show, and would I make sure it was opened an hour or so earlier for the wine to breathe. I told him to go and take a flying jump at himself. These BBC people really get my goat.

I don't know if I told you, but when the Corsican Twins were shown the door after they were thought – as it turned out incorrectly – to have buggered up the Boss's campaign in mid-election, their place at the right hand of power was taken by a curious little glue-sniffer in brothel creepers called Bell. Typical adman, flashy waistcoats, lover of food and wine, lives in a glass tower with a lot of charts and shoots a pretty good line of agency bull about targeting the under-fives etc. He's been on the blower a lot recently, yammering on about a dent in the Boss's caring image over the so-called crisis in the Health Service, i.e. a lot of bearded ragamuffins of the Extreme Left making mischief with the Florence Nightingale Brigade. (In fact Lofty Smithers, as you probably heard, flew in from Barbados in his executive jet only last week, had his gallstones shot away with one of these new space invaders machines, nurses were all over him, own room, colour telly, and it didn't cost him a penny.)

Little Bell, however, came round with his charts and diagrams, and got the Boss rattled, telling her that poking Brother Scargill in the snoot might go down well with the punters, but you couldn't do the same to tear-stained nurses

'. . . Typical adman . . .'

on *News at Ten*. Moore, M's ex-golden toyboy with the lovely eyes, huffed and puffed a good deal and said that they were not in the business of public relations, but the Boss got pretty steely, told him to shut up, and asked Bell what he thought she ought to do. Result, later the same day, enter Mr Teddy Bear with his motley gang of pot-bellied degenerates in earphones lugging their photographic equipment.

If you ask me, it didn't do her much good. Not that Mr T.B. was in danger of doing her any harm with his damnfool questions about whether she was a sensualist. Entre nous, when M. on Mr Bell's instructions started rabbiting on about how it was costing every man woman and child in the country three hundred quid a week to keep the show on the road I'm afraid I rather dozed off and woke up to find a lot of pansy actors giving each other prizes and attacking the Boss for confiscating books about Barry and Harry Want to Marry and Live With Larry. Amazing what these people in publishing get away with.

Following this fiasco, Tinker Bell seems to have fluttered round to that very unattractive one with the glasses and the gravelly voice called Hurd. You probably saw they had a big revolt at Halitosis Hall a week or so back when she whipped them into line over the Official Secrets Act. Tinker B. clearly felt that they were losing points with Hurd's closed trap policy, persuaded him to toss something off the sledge to keep the wolves at bay, and next thing Four-Eyes was on *Woman's Hour* outlining his radical new ideas, to wit everything exactly the same as before. Surprise surprise.

Meanwhile the Smellysocks have got their teeth into poor Mayhew for failing to prosecute some gallant members of the RUC who bagged a couple of Left Footers too many. Makes you sick. I said to Margaret there was no point in trying to fight the IRA in carpet slippers with both hands tied behind our backs. If they shoot to kill then we ought to do the same, and should a few rubbernecks get caught in the crossfire, that's tough. M. got very shirty, said that any damn fool could see that was what she thought, but if we said it in public we'd be up before the Court of Human Rights before you could say Blair Peach. All the Micks, inevitably, now dancing round in a Guinness-induced haze in Dublin, crying for justice. You know my view, the sooner we sever the tow-rope and let the whole bloody Emerald Isle float off into the sunset with the Leprechaun Orchestra playing 'When Irish Eyes Are Smiling' the better it will be for the human race.

I am enclosing a somewhat salacious card in padded satin with the words 'From Your Phantom Lover With Huge Hugs' which I would be grateful if you could ask your grandchild Barney to address to Mrs Nigel Lawson, Number Eleven Downing Street, London, SW1. I think a Frant postmark might create the necessary tumult in the breast of our Chancellor.

Yours ecstatically,

DENIS

Dear Bill,

You were asking me as far as I could understand on the blower last night why I'd kept you in the dark about the Boss's carpeting of Runcie and the Seven Dwarfs at Chequers last November. As I tried to explain – if you hadn't been blowing that damnfool trumpet all the time I might have succeeded – I was deliberately kept in the dark. Now that it's come out, I do remember one weekend in November when the Boss behaved very suspiciously.

I was, as I recall, lingering over breakfast, when she came bustling in with a tablecloth and an armful of knives and forks observing that I was looking out of sorts and in need of fresh air. Why didn't I ring up one or two of my friends and arrange to meet them at Huntercombe? She had already booked a table for 3 p.m. and fixed for Mr Wu to drive me there and back, the assumption being of course that I couldn't possibly find my way there without a drink and would be in no condition to find my way back after one. So seldom that one has the leash taken off voluntarily that I complied without question. But I must say my suspicions were aroused at the time and I assumed that it was to be a tete-a-tete with Smarmy C.

We are now told that it was a big showdown with Snaggle-teeth and the Bolshie Bishops. All softly softly of course, which was why Yours Truly had to be well out of the way. She clearly didn't want me sounding off over the sherry about the Pulpit Pooftahs. Margaret's technique as you know is more subtle and involved filling the victims up with bad Amontillado a la Furniss before getting out the chainsaw.

According to Wu who I rang last night it wasn't the walkover they are now making out. Snaggleteeth himself apparently tried to remain diplomatic, claiming that what she said was of great interest he was sure, but that there were two sides to every question. Then that little cricketing Johnny from Liverpool who's as Red as a baboon's bum, sounded off about the iniquities of the Poll Tax and said that if this was the Roman Empire she'd be up there in the Royal Box giving the thumbs down to Snaggellus Minimus as he disappeared down the throat of Lenny the Lion.

All of which explains what that prat Hurd has been up to over the last few days, lecturing the C of E about their moral duty in the Inner Cities. I must say the best way of rallying the country behind Runcie would be to put up Hurd and that smug little bumsucker J. Selwyn Gummer as the champions of moral decency.

The Boss got back from Brussels fit to be tied. She and Mogadon had been up all night, shouting the odds with that fat sloth Kohl and the foul-mouthed Frog Monsieur Chirac, their only supporter being some poor little Dutchman called Van der Lubbe. Despite the brave talk in the communique, it looked to me as if she and Moggers had completely caved in under the barrage of obscenity, and that we shall continue to pay nine-tenths of our hard-earned divvies to the garlic-reeking peasants and former SS corporals who follow the plough in those parts.

As if this were not enough, the Boss was buttonholed during the coffee break by that boozed-up bookie Haughey, clearly the worse for wear. He was never going to speak to her again

'. . . that mad bugger with the W. G. Grace beard who gets his orders from God . . .'

60

until justice was done to this Stalker cove, an honest copper who was sent over to sort out the RUC hit squad business and who was apparently called off p.d.q. by Hurd when he started asking awkward questions and duffed over by that mad bugger with the W. G. Grace beard who gets his orders from God. Little Stalker has now written his memoirs and been given a hero's welcome on the banks of the Liffey by the exultant Leprechauns. The Boss very unwisely in my view told Haughey to stick his head up a dead bear's bum. Net result, Irish Agreement down the khazi, Bruiser Hermon the Ulster Gang Boss rules O.K.

You know I told you to send a cod valentine to my neighbour Therese with a view to fomenting marital strife at Number Eleven? Would you believe it, some dirty sod sent the Boss an absolute Soho shocker, with the caption 'This Willie Loves You'. Boris said it must be from Whitelaw. Have you any other leads?

Yours in the antlers,

DENIS

 10 Downing Street
Whitehall
4 MARCH 1988

Dear Bill,
All is well. The mystery Valentine Card to the Boss was sent by Lawson. Boris managed to push his hand into some wet cement when he came round to talk about the Budget the other morning and the fingerprints are identical. Bloody silly trick as I had lost a good deal of sleep trying to figure out who lived in Eridge, which is where it was posted from.

Did you see that damnfool list of the richest men in the country led by H.M. the Queen? Most of them are a lot of fly-by-nights like Branson and the fat man who owns the *Daily Mirror* (we all know where *his* money comes from). Of course it's all baloney and done by levelling up the bottom line, and

I'm on the whole very glad that my name wasn't included, because you only get a lot of begging letters and people pestering you for drinks at the Club. Of course all the Left Wingers seize on that sort of thing as showing the need for greater equality. But, as I said to the Boss when we were talking to Matey Next Door about his proposals, a million pounds nowadays barely buys lunch for two in the West End, so making lists of so-called millionaires is completely pointless.

Anyway, the Boss told Lawson very firmly that there could be no question of any further handouts to the Nurses and that wealth creators such as myself must be given thumping incentives to keep the economy on the up and up. So much for Biffen and that crowd of Moaning Minnies who are always going on about the so-called have-nots. As Tebbit quite rightly said before he was led away by the men in white coats, the only reason they have-not is because they won't get up off their arses, plonk same on saddle of nearest bicycle and pedal like hell down to the Labour Exchange.

Re the Anglo-Irish Disagreement. Since my last they've barely been in their corners to spit in the bucket. Somebody clearly got the wind up about our friend Stalker, and they announced that yet another Chief Inspector was going to be detailed to dig up the bodies all over again before being duly smeared and taken off the case by the Grand Order of the Funny Handshake. This was all intended as a sop to little Haughey, who's been swinging his way round the Public Bars like a deranged orang-utang, shouting blue murder and generally blowing the froth off his Guinness. However the Mr Nice Guy approach was somewhat marred when some trigger-happy squaddy took a pot-shot at an inoffensive Paddy going about his lawful occasions. The following day they managed to reveal that another of our uniformed murderers who had been put away for life was let out after a fortnight and had been back at his sniping post for the last three years.

Poor little King, who replaced Fatty Prior in the punishment box, was by now completely out of his depth. Boss ringing him up all the time telling him to do something, some interfering Left Footer called Cardinal O'Fee howling for revenge. King hurried off to Dublin to try and bury the hatchet and have a few jars with the Big Micks. Comes out, reeling slightly and reeking of Irish Whiskey, everything tickety-boo, full and frank exchange of views, looking forward to next week's

*'. . . some interfering Left Footer called Cardinal O'Fee
howling for revenge . . .'*

meeting between Chief Inspector Handshake and the Head of
the Little People's Guard.

Immediate uproar. No such meeting agreed, back to Square
One for all concerned, Haughey now very much the worse for
wear saying things he will undoubtedly regret. Boss fit to be
tied and on the blower to the Pope telling him to get his arse
into gear and rid her of the turbulent O'Fee.

Mrs Van der K. was very full of beans in her latest aero-
gramme claiming that P.W.B. has finally cracked down on the
Trots and that he could never have done it without Margaret
being so supportive. It all seems a bit counterproductive to me
when they allow that little monkey Tutu to go on the telly
cocking a snook at the Big White Chief and flashing signals
in deaf and dumb language to Gorbo to step up the supplies
of Kalashnikovs. I was hoping to toddle down there myself
next month to tie up a few loose ends with a company I'm
nominally on the board of – for Heaven's sake not a word to
Bessie as this is a very sensitive area. Any chance of your joining me in the Executive Class? We could take in a round or
two of golf at Durban, and Mrs Van der K. promised to run
up the bunting at her husband's Leisure and Entertainment
Complex (Fun City).

I'm hoping that Smarmy C. may get his come-uppance after all. He's planning to jack up the electricity bills by 25%, and then when they're making a fat profit flog it all off to the likes of Maurice Picarda. All very well selling off the gas – oil as you may recall was pretty sticky – but can you think of anyone apart from Maurice who'd be so damn silly as to want a slice of Sizewell B a.k.a. Chernobyl-on-Sea? Nor is anyone going to buy many Rollers to dislodge 5p pieces from OAPs' meters. If anything deserves hiving off to the private sector it is our smarmy little friend C. Parkinson.

Yours in the leather apron with the trews rolled above the knee,

DENIS

10 Downing Street
Whitehall
18 MARCH 1988

Dear Bill,

I was very amused by your account of getting in the Scotch prior to Matey's Armageddon. I received a tip-off from Boris, and he and I hired a Gentle Giant DIY Removal van, drove out to that Megamarket off the M25 where fags are a penny cheaper for twenty than anywhere else in the Home Counties, and used my Cash 'n Carry Card which that chap in the House of Commons Canteen provided me with, saying I was stocking up for an Old Folks' Home in Bucks which had more than an element of truth to it. I think they should see me out. Particularly in the Boss's present mood.

The peace of Mother's Day was shattered earlier than usual by a call at 4.15 a.m. from the boy Mark in Dallas at a party given by Pa Burgerstand for his shifters of motorway scrap. His affectionate greeting to his dear mother met with a stony silence from the Boss, and when he moved on to a request for a couple of Grand to top up his overdraft the solids hit the air conditioning in no uncertain manner. Then, just after breakfast, Mr Nicely-Nicely shimmered in from next door to put the finishing touches to his Budget, tossing the usual slur at me over his shoulder about the winoes going to be badly hit as he disappeared into the sanctum.

When Boris went in with the coffee and his microfilm camera it was obvious that tempers were running high. 'It is time that we reduced interest rates, Prime Minister,' the latter-day Bunter was opining over his extensive collection of chins. 'Industry demands it. The economy demands it. Exporters demand it. I demand it.' 'Now listen to me, Nigel,' came the icy tones of the Boss. 'Inflation is, and always will be our arch enemy. I have stressed that again and again. Of course . . .' 'Oh, come off it, Prime Minister,' cried our fat friend. 'I am sick and tired of listening to you droning away week after week without a blind idea of what you're talking about. I don't need to do this job, you know. It's been quite amusing for a few years, but recently I've found it rather a strain having to listen to you nagging away like an old fishwife.'

I must say at this point I began to think I might have overlooked sterling qualities in our burly neighbour. One might quibble with the small print but the general drift seemed to be entirely sound. I sensed however that he was on the verge of encountering the killer punch. He was about to enlarge on the many hundreds of offers he had received from fat cat bankers offering him large inducements, school fees for the brawling brood next door etc in exchange for one board meeting every six months, when the Boss chimed in with a voice charged with emotion. 'Very well, Nigel, of course you must go. No, don't interrupt me. If money means more to you than serving the nation . . .' 'Oh come off it, Margaret,' interposed the former *Sunday Telegraph* share tipster, 'all that old soap may work with Cecil or little Gummer, but you are talking to a man of some intelligence. Have you read your papers today? "Perhaps the most outstanding intellect of any post-war Chancellor," says Alan Watkins. "A front-runner for the top job should anything happen to Mrs Thatcher," the *News of the World* . . .'

At this the Boss abandoned all tact and diplomacy, and the tones of the Grantham Market Place echoed through the seat of power. When Lawson emerged half an hour later he had the look of a man who had finally got things off his chest.

'There we are, Den,' he beamed, patting me on the back as he glided like a hovercraft across the hall. 'She's all yours.'

Fortunately events proved otherwise. No sooner had the spherical mastermind glowed into the fresh air, than Mr Goody Twoshoes, alias Kenneth Baker, hair all smarmed and giglamps agleam, came purring in. Do you remember that dreadful Vicar who used to collect for his Garden of Remembrance at Peasmarsh? I think the vandals did for it after the famous Oddfellows' shindig at the Lacemakers' Hall. This Baker Johnny has much the same suave and oily manner. Determined not to be taken for a sucker twice in one morning the Boss was out of her corner before the bell had even sounded. 'Now listen to me, Kenneth,' she shrilled, entering the hall at speed, 'I thought I made it clear that we want proper old-fashioned Grammar School testing from the age of seven onwards. The three Rs, tables, "Drake he's in his hammock" by heart. None of this vague socialist talk that we've inherited about continuous assessment. Were you or I "continuously assessed", Kenneth? We certainly were not. We learned our tables. We learned our spelling. And we worked away to pass our School Certificate. That is the inheritance we must pass on to our little ones. Now get out.'

'. . . "there we
are, Den," he beamed,
patting me on the back
as he glided
like a hovercraft
across the hall . . .'

Wonderful Gib being back on the SAS's battle honours. Margaret was naturally over the moon, and rang up Haughey to crow. As usual when somebody does something really decent for a change, the Smellysocks are crying stinking fish. However I have been told to stay away from Mother Flack's Time-share on the Algarve until further notice, which is rather a nuisance, there being fears of ETA reprisals on innocent wealth-creators taking their well-earned holiday breaks.

Who Dares Wines,

DENIS

10 Downing Street
Whitehall
1 APRIL 1988

Dear Bill,
Did you see the Boss scrubbing Green Park on her hands and knees? I thought the whole thing looked pretty damn silly, quite honestly. According to Boris it was our little snuff-taking friend Tinker Bell who dreamed it up with a view to boosting the Tourist Trade for the summer, many Yanks having been put off by recent events. They summoned up the reptiles, M. made the four-hundred-yard trip in an armoured Bossmobile, old cartons and condoms were scattered to a depth of about four feet on the grass and the hacks snapped away while the Boss and Ridley tried to spike it all up in two minutes like that damnfool TV *It's A Knockout* the Royals are always going on. Poor Ridley told me afterwards he'd never felt such a prat in all his life, a lot of the rubbish hadn't been washed, and he didn't like being laughed at by a lot of yobboes from the *Sun*.

I said if she wanted some extra cleaning work in the mornings why didn't she come round to the RAC where there's filth that hasn't been cleaned up since VJ Day, bags of old bottles lying round making it a real hazard finding one's way to the

Gents after lunch without falling over something. Maurice, as you may remember, went head first into the pool after the Major's Heart Surgery Lunch. But M. has always been a bit of a dustpan and brush perve. Even up here in my den she's continually dragging things out of my hands saying the dustman is outside, often bottles I have only just bought.

Poor old Goggles King got called over for a carpeting after the latest outbreak of Anglo-Irish discord. A well-meaning enough cove, who ought really to be running one of those File-O-Fax firms near Reading. Instead of which he has drawn the short straw and finds himself shunted off with all the other unemployables who seem to wind up in official positions in that Godforsaken corner of the universe. I ran into him in the hall, and he clearly mistook me for some poor old bugger collecting for Help The Aged. He started fishing in his wallet, pushed me a tenner, and then wandered off straightening his tie to run slap bang into Big M. who exploded on impact.

'What are you doing here? Why aren't you at your post?' Poor Goggles fell back, stammering about her having sent for him, but it didn't do him any good. 'I'm not here to listen to excuses, Mr King, I want solutions. It's your job to provide them.' 'Well, Prime Minister, there are a number of things we could do . . .' began the bird-like businessman. 'My own preference would be to withdraw and leave them to it . . .' 'Out of the question,' snapped the Boss. 'I have made it clear over and over again that there can be no question of yielding to the Men of Violence.' A tortured expression came over the Minister's face as he grappled with the logic of my wife's thesis and his prominent adam's apple rose and fell several times. 'Or Dublin might be encouraged to take a more responsible role . . .' 'What utter poppycock,' she ranted. 'You've seen that pathetic little Socialist Haughey. He's done everything possible to obstruct me. He even came to Strasbourg to lecture me about that crooked policeman, Stalker. How can you suggest such a thing? And why are these funerals not being properly policed by the SAS?' 'If you remember, Prime Minister, it was decided not to police . . .' 'Then it must be undecided. Come in here.'

The solid mahogany door did not prevent me from hearing what ensued. Goggles was by now sobbing loudly, and saying he had been offered a job as assistant headmaster of a preparatory school near Swanage, and couldn't Ridley do it, or anybody? Margaret must be aware he was completely powerless while rival gangs of thugs in and out of uniform re-enacted the Chicago of the Prohibition Era.

The only bright spot from where I see it is that the BBC was brought into line pretty smartish when they started rabbiting on about refusing to hand over their videotapes and the due processes of the law. As Margaret said to me when I was cleaning my teeth last night, the time for all that sort of nonsense has long since gone. The only thing the men of violence understand is a sawn-off shotgun and that, as far as she was concerned, was what they were going to get, which went for the BBC as well.

'. . . Benn's mind, as I think I told you, has been rotted away by tea . . .'

Pillock has caused some rejoicing at Smith Square now he's going to have to do battle with the Knight of the Revolving Eyes, Sir Loonie de Benn and his faithful squire Eric the Heifer. Benn's mind, as I think I told you, has been rotted away by tea and he is now totally barmy, so it could be quite an amusing scrap. Maurice is offering 11–3 on Kinnock, and taking side bets on Hattersley being unseated by Eric the H.

If only Matey next door could be persuaded to throw his homburg into the ring while he's still fuming. Are we still meeting at Gatwick on Good Friday? They've moved the Duty Free apparently to the New Underwater Lounge in Terminal 14, so I'd get there early if you want to get your sea-legs before takeoff. Charlie Whackett's sending out a limo to pick us up at Managua and we're meeting for lunch at somewhere called the Contra Club House which I gather is some way up country.

Hasta la vista, muchacho,

DENIS

10 Downing Street
Whitehall

15 APRIL 1988

Dear Bill,

Charlie Whackett flew in on the Concorde on Wednesday, saying his journey had been made intolerable by some awful little reformed piss-artist working for an English newspaper in Washington who insisted on making conversation, laced with exhortations to abandon the demon drink. Apparently Charlie spun him some far-fetched yarn about how he was on his way to China to hire a tramp steamer boat for ferrying rock down the East Coast to line the Channel Tunnel with. Little fellow in the waistcoat swallowed it h. l. and s. and wrote it up the next day in his paper. Amazing how these Johnnies fill up their columns.

Charlie is full of stories about Hoppo. As you know the Old Gunslinger is totally gaga and puts his trousers on back to front so often they've had to fit flies on both sides. But the amazing thing is that the Yanks are still rooting for him, so much so that his number two, a fairly dim cove called George, is almost bound to get the job when Hoppo's final farewell tour comes to an end. The other side cannot make their minds up between a Greek shyster called Dukokup and a frisky little coon in a dog-collar called Jessie James. Whatever you say about the Land of the Free, it does seem quite a sensible idea to set a time-limit to holding down the top job. The same thought has clearly been crossing what passes for the mind of Mr Munster a.k.a. N. Tebbit Esq. who, when not lecturing the Royals on their duties, has been busy denying that he has any intention of stepping into Margaret's high-heeled shoes. But he and Matey are, according to Boris, regularly seen lunching at the Quat' Saisons, a very fancy foodery out in the sticks with private rooms. Boris says that MI5 have now bugged all the tables, so we should be getting full transcripts in the near future.

None of this has pleased the Boss by any manner of means. What really got her goat was that bunch of Communists at Amnesty International, who had the cheek to ask for an enquiry into the SAS job in Gibraltar. I was unlucky to be within earshot when Tinker Bell waddled unsteadily in with the tickertape. The Old Girl really hit the roof, and is still picking the Axminster out of her teeth. Quite rightly too in my opinion. I mean what's the world coming to when our knights in shining armour can't ride forth to pump hot lead into the Paddy without a lot of bearded do-gooders cluck-clucking in their evil-smelling underground offices. Her immediate reaction was to let the SAS abseil into Amnesty Headquarters and take them out, beards and all, but I advised caution. These things have a way of going off at half cock, and you may remember the fellow last time who got the rope tangled round his Y-fronts at the Iranian Embassy. Talking of bugging, they got some quite good tapes from Transport House, where Bedlam reigns. Even on Boris's new hi-fi system it's very hard to make out the voices, but the penny finally seems to have dropped re Brer Pillock, i.e. Friend Gingernuts is never going to make it to the executive toilet at Chequers. You or I could have told them that years ago. For all the good he's done them they could just as well have stuck with that nice old geezer in the pebble glasses whose buttons were always coming off at the Cenotaph. Now there is a queue of likely lads trying to nobble the fat one in the Number Two Seat, and Pillock having set up all this damnfool machinery for having elections in the party every five minutes is well and truly hoist with his own whatsit. Serve the little bugger right

71

'. . . that bunch of Communists
at Amnesty International . . .'

is my view. According to Boris, they'll pick either a Scottish lawyer called Smith or a New Zealand accountant called Gold, or it may be the other way round.

I almost forgot. Our Easter was completely spoilt by that atheist Bishop who failed to get the message when his cathedral burst into flames. He had the damn insolence to lay into Margaret just because she's tightened up the rules about supplementary benefit. Everybody knows perfectly well there are millions of druggie scroungers raking it in while hard-working chaps like you and me have to foot the bill. I said if the SAS wanted a bit of exercise, Durham would make an ideal target. They could scramble the whole complex to Kingdom Come just like they did in that Navarone business during the '39 Show.

Yours in Excelsis,

DENIS

10 Downing Street
Whitehall

13 MAY 1988

Dear Bill,

I did enjoy our few days off the leash on the Cote d'Azur. Some splendid golf, and your accountant friend Pringle certainly knows his way round the night spots. What was the name of that restaurant where he poured champagne over the manageress? Beau something or other up in some sort of a slate quarry? No matter, but I think I may have left my trousers there.

The Boss has been fit to be tied all week over the antics of those TV Trots trying to make mischief out of Our Boys' spectacular bag in Gib. We all know perfectly well that it was the best thing that ever happened when those three Paddies bit the dust. As the Major was saying only the other night, why can't they do that to everyone with any connection with the IRA, we'd soon have the whole problem solved. But of course our little bearded friends on television, all working on instructions from Moscow, are seeing it as a golden opportunity to throw mud at the Boss in the hope that some of it will stick. A whole lot of so-called witnesses, i.e. tarts, spies, fly-by-nights, the usual riff-raff you see hanging around outside the NAAFI in those parts, were all prepared to swear they saw our men in black roar up and plug them in the kidneys. Even if they did, so what? As that very nice Belgian bloke with the blue rinse said in the *Sunday Telegraph*, 'Shoot them down like rats, that's the only language they understand.'

What sticks in Margaret's craw, as she said in the House, is these TV buggers interfering with the rule of law. (Entre nous, I thought it a bit rich to talk about the rule of law when rubbing out the opposition in the best Mafia style, but I wisely kept the trap well buttoned.) Incidentally, there is some displeasure here with little Hurd, who has made himself conspicuous as Home Secretary by not joining in the general arse-kicking of Hussey and Co. I did break silence to issue a warning to M. on that one, as I wouldn't put it past him to be doing a Heseltine on the quiet.

Talking of arses, the most extraordinary little Brummy spiv

with an oiled quiff came round last week from the *Sunday Times*. Boris tells me he used to be with the Smellysocks but decided to go for gold, cleaned up on the TV and has now retired to some off-shore tax haven. I've seen some fawning in my day, as you can imagine, but this little creamer took the biscuit. As I said to Boris, it was a damn good thing he'd written his name on the soles of his shoes or we'd never have seen him again.

Re Hoppo's alarming descent into the world of soothsayers and mystics, I blame the emaciated spouse. I always thought she was a rum 'un. I don't know if I told you, but the first time we stayed in Washington she came into my dressing room one night before dinner when I was reading the *Telegraph* and asked if she could see my hand. I thought it was a pretty odd way to go on at the time, but she pored over the palm for some minutes drawing a hand across her brow, then told me I had married a forceful dynamic woman, and that I had two great loves in my life. I asked what the other one was, and she said she saw a group of men walking over the grass with little white balls.

'. . . she came into my dressing room . . . and asked if she could see my hand . . .'

74

Boris has just gone out to Interflora on M's behalf to send a bouquet of English roses to the French President on his re-election. I asked her why she was so keen on a Pinko, and she said the French nation was in no mood for change, and that age was no bar to the retention of high office, that on the contrary the passing of the years brought only wisdom and serenity.

God help us all.

Au revoir, Enfants de la Patrie,

DENIS

 10 Downing Street
Whitehall
27 MAY 1988

Dear Bill,

Sorry I couldn't get over to St Andrews for your Burmah reunion with Wino Podsnap. I'm glad to hear it all went well despite the brush with the Constabulary when Wino stole the earth-mover.

As you probably saw from the papers, I was pretty tied up with the Boss's Billy Graham Campaign to win back the Scots. For some time North of the Tweed has been a no-go area for our lot, with Kinnock's men ruling the glens in 49 varieties of Trotskyist tartan and only coming South to hurl the furniture about in the H of C and get into showers with young women. (Talking of which, I was very relieved that Maurice managed to elude the *Sunday People* photographers outside his club in Wigmore Street, unlike, I am told, some former close associates of the Boss (no names no packdrill), who are even now negotiating for the return of the negatives.)

Be that as it may, little Tinker Bell, our hyperactive snuff-taking friend from the advertising agency, felt that the time had come to hammer the Scots back into the fold. His first scheme, which turned out to be a pretty damp squib, was for M. to hand over the Scottish FA Cup at the final. According to little Bell's plan, all the kilted hooligans would respond like monkeys to the sight of the Trophy and the cameras would roll, giving the impression the Boss was getting a standing ovation. In the event, the Men in Blue advised that for security reasons M. was going to have to press the flesh with the players in the shower room. Result, ninety minutes of boredom for yours truly watching twenty-two unidentifiable Scottish louts hacking one another in the bollocks, followed by an embarrassing scene in which my good lady handed over the Cup to some evil-smelling little rebel of unintelligible brogue while eighty thousand inebriates sang the Red Flag and showered beercans on the roof.

Plan B. This particularly appealed to the Boss for two reasons. First, Scots a pastor-ridden society, led by a bunch of penny-pinching old misers like her revered father the late Alderman Roberts. Having convinced the shepherds that she was a chip off the old block, the sheep, albeit half-pissed, would soon follow. At the same time she could rub the Bishop of Durham's nose in it good and proper.

Bell hired for this purpose a clerical crasher from Cambridge, a bespectacled man in a suit who asked for Perrier water without lemon and then dictated a few notes to the effect that the Bible was all basically on our side, i.e. blessed are the Wealth Creators and sod the rest of them. Even little Bell however found some of the finer points of theology a bit over his head, so Brer Bore was shown into the Typing Pool to tap out M's Sermon on the Olivetti. The result was a pretty good dog's breakfast which the Boss had the greatest difficulty in reading off the prompter screens while I sat among the crows having frequent recourse to the Queen Mother's flask.

Afterwards, however, over warm sherry in the Moderator's changing room she was very bucked, and said it would show Hurd who was top dog in the Sermon Handicap. Between ourselves, little Doug has been sniffing round the throne for some weeks making prophetic utterances about moral responsibility etc with a view to capturing the spiritual high ground prior to mounting a night attack from the rear. Give me Munster any day of the week, as the masseuse said when she saw Major Ron coming back for the ninth time.

'. . . Bell hired for this purpose a clerical crasher from Cambridge . . .'

Hurd is not the only one to have been uppity of late. Our fat friend next door has been trumpeting around saying he has forced Margaret to eat humble pie over interest rates. In my view he'd never have done it without the support of Mogadon Man, who to everyone's amazement suddenly came out of his coma and began thumping the table in support of Mr Nicely. Apparently the Boss was so taken aback by Mogadon coming to that she caved in on all fronts. But if you ask me it was her own fault for infuriating Howe when she told that little greaser Walden there was no one in her Cabinet of any calibre and that the one she really fancied was Dr David Owen.

If Daphne insists on coming up for the Flower Show why not slip the leash and join me at the RAC for a pre-lunch drink about ten-thirty? Failing that I could meet you in the Fison's Slugdeath Tent and we could sink a few schooners of the product on site.

Yours herbaceously,

DENIS

10 Downing Street
Whitehall
10 JUNE 1988

Dear Bill,

Sorry I had to leave a note for you at the Rotary Lunch but we were obliged to turn out for Red Carpet Duty, i.e. return of Conquering Hero and emaciated spouse at Heathrow following their triumphant Farewell Benefit Concert at the Moscow Essoldo.

The old boy fell off the plane more alive than dead, but only just, kissed me on both cheeks, ignoring Margaret, and said, 'Bonjour Monsieur le President.' At this the Boss, who has gone very cool on her old pin-up now that he's only got a few months between him and the garbage truck, gripped him firmly by the arm and steered him into the back of the nearest limo, tut-tutting and looking at her watch. We then drove back to HQ for the so-called de-briefing. While M. and Hoppo went off to the Den I was stuck as per usual with the aforementioned E.S. Moscow, she told me, was a truly wonderful place, full of very beautiful people of such warmth and profound religious feeling it brought tears to her eyes. 'Do you know, Sir Geoffrey, we were taken to one of Russia's old churches, and to see these truly wonderful old monks with their white beards chanting their age-old Russian church music, why it was just like *Doctor Zhivago* come to life.' I decided to stir it at this point by saying how much I liked Mrs Gorbo, adding that I found her both attractive and sympathetic. Sure enough the First Lady's eyes became diamond hard. 'My dear, a typical Capricorn subject with Sagittarius on the cusp. I felt very sorry for her. No style, no conversation. Of course in the Free World she would have the benefit of a first rate analyst, but they are so behind, so backward over there. And she's so brave about having no clothes or proper jewellery.'

I didn't have to say much more after that and was able to nod sagely over a large refill as she wove variations on the theme. When the Boss finally led poor old Hoppo out of the Den, still grinning from ear to ear and clutching his Duty Free, I could tell that Anglo-American relations, at least from

78

her point of view, were not at their perkiest. After the old gunslinger had waddled off M. fair exploded. 'He is just a film star, of course. He can go on TV and do his act, and simple people are taken in. But the Russians respect firmness. Of course when I went there, there was no time for any showbusiness flim-flam. It was all tough talking. Decisions were made that affected the future of the world. Anyway, at seventy-seven, it is too much to expect a man to have his faculties about him.'

'. . . *catching a few winks . . . while some crasher with a beard was droning on about the future of the Russian novel . . .*'

I must say I couldn't help sympathising with the old boy when I saw him catching a few winks on the TV while some crasher with a beard was droning on about the future of the Russian novel. I had a chance to express solidarity while he was being helped into his coat in the lobby. I slipped him a couple of miniatures for the trip back to the airport, and he said, 'I want you to know, Frank, that you'd sure as hell be welcome on the Ranch any time you want to get away from that woman. What a ball-breaker!'

Meanwhile the Turbulent Priests of the Golden Temple have refused to give up despite heavy shelling by the Boss. The Bishop of Gloucester, a prat in glasses to you and me, was clearly determined to go to the stake under Bloody Margaret for his undying belief in the welfare state, and wrote out two thousand words of BULL that he nailed to the door of Central Office. Unfortunately nobody gave a monkey's, apart from the Boss, who was at work upstairs with her Cambridge Bore trying her hand at another sermon. I told her she should make it clear to Runcie that if there was any more insolence she'd see to it that sidekick of his with the beard who went missing a couple of years back would stay there for good.

You have to hand it to Margaret's little fellow Ingham who tosses rotting tit-bits to the reptiles every morning. As you probably saw, the Pinkoes got their Y-fronts in a twist over the Gib Inquest. Friend Bernard got up cool as a cucumber, and told them that there was unfortunately a Local Dog Show that clashed, so it would have to be postponed till August. What he'd cleverly worked out, you see, was that all those idle piss-artists from Fleet Street, together with the Marxists from Halitosis Hall, would all be on holiday by then, with the added advantage, as I pointed out to Barmy Hoddinott at the RAC, that our Hit Squad will as like as not be on holiday as well, so they won't be available to give evidence even if they wanted to.

Boris tells me that Prince Charles's friend Mr Hammer who used to work for Lenin is going to build a Golf Course outside Moscow. Could this mean that they really are changing things over there?

A large Glasnost on the rocks to you, Comrade,

DENIS